The Gift of Health

As a dentist, I have dedicated my life to helping people enjoy the best possible oral health.

Achieving this goal requires a joint effort between members of the dental team and their patients.

This lovely book is given to you as a gentle reminder to help reach the goal by continuing to:

☺ Brush your teeth at least twice daily,

☺ Floss at least once daily, and

☺ Visit this office for checkups and teeth cleaning at least twice a year.

If we work together, you can enjoy a lifetime of healthy smiles.

You may contact our office at:

D1383100

What People Are Saying About
Chicken Soup for the Dental Soul . . .

"From one dentist to another—read this book! And ask every patient who walks in your door to read it. The truth and warmth of *Chicken Soup for the Dental Soul* will bring dentists and patients closer together."

Steven Novick, DDS

"I enjoyed reading all the stories in *Chicken Soup for the Dental Soul.* Some made me laugh, some made me cry, and many of them touched my heart. I came away with a new appreciation of the opportunity we have every day to connect with another person and make a difference in their lives."

Gary D. Sellers, DDS

"*Chicken Soup for the Dental Soul* will make you laugh and cry, smile and frown. It is a very honest and heartwarming look into the real world of dentistry. This book is truly the right filling for your dental soul."

Ira Marder, DDS, FAGD

"Reading the stories turned out to be a mini-dental education in itself. I learned a great deal from these heartwarming stories. They touch your mind, heart, and soul—truly *Chicken Soup for the* Dental *Soul.*"

Robert S. Quintano, DDS

"*Chicken Soup for the Dental Soul* is the first publication to show the human, poignant, and oftentimes humorous side of dentistry."

Danny Gerstner, DDS

"I now recommend brushing, flossing, and at least a daily dose of *Chicken Soup for the Dental Soul* to all of my patients!"

Timothy G. Donley, DDS, MSD

"Reading *Chicken Soup for the Dental Soul* has brought me laughter and tears, both of which are definitely good for the soul. It has been an honor and a blessing to be associated with the high caliber of people who make up the dental profession. I challenge both patient and practitioner to try and put this book down once you have started to read the inspiring stories."

Dennis J. Michaelson, DMD, MS

"*Chicken Soup for the Dental Soul* is wonderful! It will take the fear out of dental cowards and make all patients see dentists and dental hygienists as caring human beings."

Merritt D. Halem, DDS

"How very gratifying to read about, and belong to, a group who are the most conscientious, dedicated, caring, and giving professionals in the world! Thank you, *Chicken Soup for the Dental Soul.*"

Jeffrey M. Galler, DDS, FAGD

"Every one of us have had patients who have touched our soul. Reading *Chicken Soup for the Dental Soul* rekindles those emotions and reminds us of why we are in the profession."

Gary E. Heyamoto, DDS, FAGD

"Dentists are 'itching' to tell their stories; and I guarantee you lots of tears and belly laughs from those within the covers of *Chicken Soup for the Dental Soul.*"

Charles W. Kenney, DDS

"*Chicken Soup for the Dental Soul* is a collection of light-hearted stories that will have readers laughing, crying, and wondering, 'When was the last time I saw my dentist?' "

Jim Park, DDS

"At last, documented proof that dentists enjoy *helping* people, and causing pain is the *last* thing we try to do. I now believe there *is* a Tooth Fairy thanks to *Chicken Soup for the Dental Soul.*"

Oscar Goren, DMD

CHICKEN SOUP
FOR THE
DENTAL SOUL

Heartwarming, Funny, and Inspiring Stories for Dental Patients, Dentists, Dental Hygienists, and the Entire Dental Team

Jack Canfield
Mark Victor Hansen
Don Dible

Health Communications, Inc.
Deerfield Beach, Florida

www.hci-online.com
www.chickensoup.com

We would like to acknowledge the following publishers and individuals for permission to reprint the following material.

The Secret Element. Reprinted by permission of Oscar Goren, DMD. ©1999 Oscar Goren.

Body and Soul. Reprinted by permission of Luz Abrera-Crum, DDS. ©1999 Luz Abrera-Crum.

Rainbow Child. Reprinted by permission of Diane Stefanowicz, RDH. ©1999 Diane Stefanowicz.

Mrs. Jackson. Reprinted by permission of Katharine A. Simmons, RDH. ©1999 Katharine A. Simmons.

Johnny. Reprinted by permission of Danny Gerstner, DDS. ©1999 Danny Gerstner.

Christmas Roses. Reprinted by permission of Lenora P. Rutledge, RDH. ©1999 Lenora P. Rutledge.

Lola's Nose. Reprinted by permission of Michael C. Goldman, DDS. ©1999 Michael C. Goldman.

More Than Skin Deep. Reprinted by permission of Jay L. Wolff, DDS. ©1999 Jay L. Wolff.

Annie's New Smile. Reprinted by permission of Julie Karnazes, DDS. ©1999 Julie Karnazes.

(Continued on page 202)

Publisher: Health Communications, Inc.
                 3201 S.W. 15th Street
                 Deerfield Beach, FL 33442-8190

Cover illustrations of Tooth Fairy, Alligator, and Star Field courtesy of American Business Card, Scottsdale, Arizona, (800) 555-2234. ©1997 American Business Card.

Cover design by Dible Associates

Contents

4. ON KINDNESS AND CARING

5. FOREIGN INTRIGUE

6. KIDS AT THE DENTAL OFFICE

7. MEMORABLE PATIENTS

8. OVERCOMING OBSTACLES

9. ECLECTIC WISDOM

Acknowledgments

Where to begin? So many people helped make this book happen, it's hard to decide. Let's start with a huge round of hugs, high fives, and thank you's to our families.

To Mark's wife, Patty, who constantly supports his writing and editing efforts, and to his daughters, Elisabeth and Melanie, who share their dad with his work.

To Jack's son, Christopher, for sharing his dad with us.

To Don's wife, Alice, who has provided nonstop encouragement and support during the more than eighteen months it's taken to bring this project from concept to completed manuscript. She listened enthusiastically as Don shared hundreds of the more than 1,200 stories received as *Chicken Soup for the Dental Soul* candidates. Her patience, thoughtful feedback, and candid opinions on many elements in the production of the manuscript had a significant impact on early story selection and the content of the Introduction. Her volunteer efforts immediately prior to the "editing blitz" at which the final stories, cartoons, and quotes were selected and sequenced is deeply appreciated.

To Alice and Don's son, Max, an accomplished guitarist and composer/transcriber who took time out to help his dad during periods of overload by providing urgent messenger services to the Post Office, Federal Express, and UPS.

To Bob Bush, Alice's late father, who lived with the Dible's during his final months on Earth, and whose early encouragement prepared Don for the rigors of work on *Chicken Soup for the Dental Soul*.

We also wish to acknowledge the following people:

Don's dentist, Rudi Neumarker, DDS, who, over lunches at the California Café not far from his dental practice on the Stanford University campus, during the restoration of a chipped front tooth, and while removing a pesky popcorn hull lodged between one of Don's molars and the tongue side of his gum, managed to provide encouragement, professional insight, and valued recommendations for this project.

Sandy Westenberger, RDH, President-elect of the Wisconsin Dental Hygienist's Association and Judy Nist, RDH, President of the Vermont Dental Hygienist's Association, both of whom were enormously patient while helping Don understand the role of dental hygienists in the dental field.

Dee Curreri, Merv Fetzer, Jim Halcomb, Kathleen Hawkins, Gerardo Joffe, Bill Kern, Calder Lowe, Sid McDonald, Dick Norman, Ace Remas, Jerry Richardson, Aytch Roberts, Stephen Seligman and Beth Greer, George and Mickey Tralle, Peter A. Turla, Cinda Voegtli, and Bob and Betty Wroe for simply "being there" for Don.

Patty Aubery, President of Chicken Soup for the Soul Enterprises, Inc., for her role in the final round of story, cartoon, and quote selection and sequencing while at the same time managing the day-to-day activities of the staff of The Canfield Group and Self-Esteem Seminars and mothering her new son, Chandler Scott.

Nancy Autio for her role in rounding up the difficult copyright permissions required for our cartoons.

Rochelle Pennington for an outstanding job of finding additional, last minute quotes with which to enrich our stories.

Dave White at Digital DNA for exceptional work in his creative design of the *Chicken Soup for the Dental Soul* cover title.

Behrooz Behzadi and Akbar Hosseini at Linographics who provided their unique computer talents in assisting Don with technical aspects of the cover design.

Ross Mostofi at American Copy for bailing Don out with numerous last-minute photocopying and binding tasks.

Jason Y. Koo at Galaxy Printing & Lithography Co. for producing reader review copies of our semi-finalist manuscript and official *Chicken Soup for the Dental Soul* stationary.

Holly Brady, Director of The Stanford Professional Publishing Course, for her beyond-the-call-of-duty assistance at last year's Executive Refresher Course.

Jim Otis of Bay Area Press for answering lots of Don's dumb questions about printing.

Dan Poynter of Para Publishing for answering lots of Don's dumb questions about publishing.

Luz Abrera-Crum, DDS; Ira Biderman, DDS; Laurence M. Brownstein, DDS; Mitchell J. Burgin, DDS; Andrew Christopher, DDS, MHA; Edwin T. Coleman, DDS; Andrew P. Collins, DMD; Ron Cummings, DDS; Eric K. Curtis, DDS, MAGD; Susan R. Cushing, DMD, CHt; Ralph E. Dendler, DDS; Thomas G. Dwyer, DDS, MS; Christopher Freyermuth, DMD; Jeffrey M. Galler, DDS, FAGD; Alan H. Gelbert, DDS, FAGD; Danny Gerstner, DDS; Darrel J. Gilbert, DDS; Oscar Goren, DMD; Leon S. Grabow, DDS; John R. Grasso, DDS; Michael H. Halasz, DDS; Merritt D. Halem, DDS; Sheila Hall, DDS; Robert J. Harland, DMD; D. Michael Hart, DDS, MAGD; Gary E. Heyamoto, DDS, FAGD; John J. Johnson, DDS; Julie Karnazes, DDS; Lawrence B. Keithly, DDS; Charles W. Kenney, DDS; Sol Kutler, DDS; Rochelle G. Lindemeyer, DMD; Ann Madigan, DMD, MSc; Richard W. Marcus, DDS; Ira Marder, DDS, FAGD; Gregory V. McGowan, DDS; Fred Melton, DDS; Stephen J. Meraw, DDS, MS; Dennis Michaelson, DMD, MS; Thomas K. Murphy, DDS; Nancy Myerson, DMD; Rudi Neumarker, DDS;

David B. Nibouar, DMD, FAGD; Steven Novick, DDS; Mary M. O'Connor, DDS; Jim Park, DDS; Norman A. Patterson, DDS; Susan Paurazas, DDS, MHSA, MS; Thomas K. Poore, DDS, MS; Robert S. Quintano, DDS; Robert Reyto, DDS, FAACD; John W. Robinson, DDS, FAGD; Michael A. Sanford, DMD; Steven Schwartz, DDS; Gary D. Sellers, DDS; Brad Shwidock, DMD; Teri Steinberg, DDS; Gregory H. Wahl, DDS; Lloyd A. Wallin, DDS; Jane L. O'Ban Walpole, DDS; Rick Waters, DMD; Lisa M. Wendell, DDS; Jeffrey L. Wissot, DDS, FAGD; Jay L. Wolff, DDS; and Lawrence Yanover, DDS, PhD for evaluating 160 semi-finalist manuscripts from which the stories in this book were selected.

Ira Biderman, DDS; Gloria Bowen, RDH; Mitchell J. Burgin, DDS; Andrew Christopher, DDS, MHA; Edwin T. Coleman, DDS; Susan R. Cushing, DMD, CHt; Ellen Dietz, CDA, BS; Eleanor Doff; Beverly E. Downs, RDH; Thomas G. Dwyer, DDS, MS; Ladd Ellis, DDS; Becky Fontenot, CDA; Sherrie Frame; Marlene George; Michael C. Goldman, DDS; Adrienne Gonzales, RDH; Merritt D. Halem, DDS; Cindy Harker, RDH; Robert J. Harland, DMD; Gary E. Heyamoto, DDS, FAGD; Howard Hornstein, DDS; Joseph G. Kalil, DDS; Lawrence B. Keithly, DDS; Charles W. Kenney, DDS; Christy King, RDH; Michell D. King, DDS; Sonya Koehler; Marla Leibfried, CDA; Philip D. Marano, DDS; Fred Melton, DDS; Kimberly Morantes, RDH; Betty Moss; Sandra C. Nelson; Rudi Neumarker, DDS; Sue O'Brien, RDH; Norman A. Patterson, DDS; Jackie S. Perry, RDH; Mary Jo Pletz; Thomas K. Poore, DDS, MS; Robert S. Quintano, DDS; Lenora P. Rutledge, RDH; Gary D. Sellers, DDS; Rosalyn Shraiar, RDH; Brad Shwidock, DMD; Diane Stefanowicz, RDH; Peter A. Turla; Gregory H. Wahl, DDS; Lloyd A. Wallin, DDS; Jane L. O'Ban Walpole, DDS; Rick Waters, DMD; and Rex Yanase for submitting a truly fascinating variety of dental-specific quotation suggestions.

Luz Abrera-Crum, DDS; Ira Biderman, DDS; Laurence M. Brownstein, DDS; Mitchell J. Burgin, DDS; Andrew Christopher, DDS, MHA; Edwin T. Coleman, DDS; Andrew P. Collins, DMD; Ron Cummings, DDS; Eric K. Curtis, DDS, MAGD; Ralph E. Dendler, DDS; Timothy G. Donley, DDS, MSD; Christopher Freyermuth, DMD; Jeffrey M. Galler, DDS, FAGD; Alan H. Gelbert, DDS, FAGD; Danny Gerstner, DDS; Michael C. Goldman, DDS; John R. Grasso, DDS; Merritt D. Halem, DDS; Sheila Hall, DDS; Cindy Harker, RDH; Robert J. Harland, DMD; Gary E. Heyamoto, DDS, FAGD; Julie Karnazes, DDS; Charles W. Kenney, DDS; Ann Madigan, DMD, MSc; Richard W. Marcus, DDS; Ira Marder, DDS, FAGD; Gregory V. McGowan, DDS; Fred Melton, DDS; Stephen J. Meraw, DDS, MS; Dennis Michaelson, DMD, MS; Thomas K. Murphy, DDS; Nancy Myerson, DMD; Rudi Neumarker, DDS; Steven Novick, DDS; Mary M. O'Connor, DDS; Jim Park, DDS; Norman A. Patterson, DDS; Thomas K. Poore, DDS, MS; Robert S. Quintano, DDS; John W. Robinson, DDS, FAGD; Michael A. Sanford, DMD; Steven Schwartz, DDS; Gary D. Sellers, DDS; Teri Steinberg, DDS; Lloyd A. Wallin, DDS; Jane L. O'Ban Walpole, DDS; Rick Waters, DMD; Lisa M. Wendell, DDS; Jeffrey L. Wissot, DDS, FAGD; Jay L. Wolff, DDS; and Lawrence Yanover, DDS, PhD for their thoughtful comments regarding early proposals for our Tooth Fairy cover design.

The *Chicken Soup* reader panel consisting of Fred Angelis, Chell and Lisa Atchley, Nancy Autio, Ken Brown, K. Collins, Patrick Collins, Julie Garner, Barbara LoMonaco, Linda Mitchell, Robbin O'Neill, and Noah St. John. Members of this elite group each read and grade an average of more than 2,000 candidate stories every year and have extraordinary insight into the types of stories our faithful *Chicken Soup for the Soul* series fans enjoy.

The dental professionals, their families and friends, that submitted more than 1,200 dental related stories for publication consideration in this book. You know who you are. While many of the stories submitted were wonderful, most did not fit into the overall structure of the book. We received so many excellent stories, we made our final selections by relying heavily on the recommendations of our regular *Chicken Soup* reader panel named above as well as 64 dentists, also named above, that somehow found the time in their hectic schedules to read and grade 160 semi-finalist stories.

Clayton Luz, Staff Writer with the *ADA News,* and the editors of 177 other dental newsletters, bulletins, magazines, journals, and e-zines that helped us bring our call for stories to the attention of members of the dental profession throughout the United States and parts of Canada. The combined circulation of these publications exceeded 500,000 and was directly responsible for our receiving so many fine stories.

Peggy Bernes, Executive Director of the Marin County Dental Society; Gregory Kaveney, Executive Director of the Seattle King County Dental Society; Francis Miliano, Executive Director of the Maine Dental Association; and Ruth Ludeman, Director of the National Association of Dental Assistants; each of whom sent us clever, funny, dental specific cartoons that had previously been featured in publications of their respective organizations. Diane Brucato-Thomas, RDH, EF, BS; Shari Jay, RDH, and Leslie Forbes were also kind enough to recommend a number of cartoons, several of which are included in this book.

Due to the scope of this project, we may have left out the names of some people who helped us out along the way. If so, we are truly sorry. Please know that we really appreciate all of you.

We are sincerely grateful for the many hands and hearts that made this book possible. We love you all!

Introduction

When we first invited dentists, dental hygienists, dental assistants, other dental office personnel, and their friends and relatives to send us *Chicken Soup for the Soul®* type stories, we had no way of knowing just what to expect. However, from the very beginning we have been touched by the warm, poignant, sometimes cute, and often funny content of what we've received. All of these stories are about dental professionals and their patients—dental patients who very well may be just like you!

What we—and the readers who helped us screen more than 1,200 candidate stories submitted for this book—have discovered is truly fascinating. The content of these dental stories is just as heartwarming, just as humorous, and every bit as satisfying as those in the 25 previously published *Chicken Soup for the Soul* books you may already have read, enjoyed, and purchased for friends as gifts.

Having said that, we want you to know that *Chicken Soup for the Dental Soul* is *totally different* from any other *Chicken Soup* book. Not only will these stories open your heart and rekindle your spirits, they will also make you aware of, in ways you never dreamed about, the importance of your teeth. Yes, that's what we said, your *teeth*!

When we decided to produce *Chicken Soup for the Dental Soul*, we wanted to do more than honor our tradition of bringing another group of absolutely wonderful stories to our loyal readers. We asked ourselves if there wasn't some way we could entertain and, at the same time, increase reader awareness of the importance of good oral health. If you wish, you may regard this book as an experiment.

We have no doubt you will enjoy *Dental Soul*—the high marks assigned these stories by our reader panel virtually guarantee that. However, we dare you to read every story in this book without making the decision to take better care of your oral health and spread the word to your friends and loved ones. If you or someone you know is "allergic" to visiting the dental office, this book can help turn you and them around for a lifetime of improved checkups.

Consider this: Almost all of us have teeth. And if we care for them properly, each one of us may enjoy the benefits of keeping all, or almost all, of our pearly whites—for a lifetime. Healthy, attractive teeth and gums can make us physically appealing and more acceptable to others. There's absolutely nothing quite so irresistible—and contagious—as a broad, warm, *sparkling* smile.

People with healthy teeth rarely offend others with bad breath. Healthy teeth can have a profound effect on our self-esteem. Since they enable us to chew our food, teeth are an important element in our nutrition as well as our enjoyment and appreciation of fine, well prepared meals. Unhealthy teeth and gums may not only cause us pain, they can become infected and, by way of our bloodstream, spread that infection throughout our entire body.

The surest way to have trouble with your teeth is to neglect them. For most people, regular brushing and flossing and proper diet can go a long way toward helping ensure healthy teeth and gums. However, important as it is, good homecare alone is no guarantee of long-term oral health.

Periodic visits to the dental office to have your teeth professionally cleaned and your mouth examined by a dentist are key elements in your holistic wellbeing. The condition of the mouth—including teeth, gums, soft palate, cheeks, lips, and tongue—provide the dentist with important clues as to the health of the rest of your body. It is not at all unusual for dentists to refer patients to other healthcare professionals based on symptoms that initially appear in the mouth due to anemia and other blood disorders, vitamin and mineral deficiencies, allergies, certain types of cancer, etc.

One last thing. We've already told you that the stories in this book are about dental professionals and their patients. All of the stories are true. However, as a professional courtesy the names of some of the patients and a few of the dentists—but not all—have been changed by request to protect their privacy. We have omitted notification in those individual stories affected so as not to interfere with your reading pleasure.

So what are you waiting for? We invite you to open a box of Kleenex—many of these poignant stories will make you cry; others will bring you to tears from laughing. Be sure to have your toothbrush, toothpaste, and dental floss handy—you may be overcome by an irresistible impulse to brush and floss. Go for it! May we suggest you begin reading...*NOW?*

Share with Us

We would like to know your reactions to the stories in this book. Please drop us a line by mail or email and indicate what your favorite stories were and how they affected you.

We also invite you to send us stories you would like to have considered for publication in our upcoming *2nd Helping of Chicken Soup for the Dental Soul*. This invitation is extended to all dental professionals as well as dental patients—in other words, just about anyone with a great dentistry-related story to share.

You can send us either stories you have written or stories written by others. But be sure to put your mailing address on all submissions. You may also include your phone number. If you send us stories written by others, please be sure to provide information on how we may contact the author. Thanks.

Send submissions to:

Chicken Soup for the Dental Soul
P.O Box 30880
Santa Barbara, CA 93130
To email us, visit our Web site at:
www.chickensoup.com

We hope you enjoy reading this book as much as we enjoyed compiling, editing, and writing it.

1

ON LOVE AND FRIENDSHIP

Duty calls us to do things well, but love makes us do them beautifully.

Phillips Brooks

The Secret Element

I like not only to be loved, but to be told *that I am loved; the realm of silence is large enough beyond the grave.*

George Eliot

When Susan called to say she needed help with a broken tooth, I was confused since she managed the office of another dentist. She told me that her boss, Dr. Benjamin Karp, had been ill and was in the hospital.

While I repaired Susan's broken tooth, I realized I simply was not qualified to fix what was really broken. Ben was dying of cancer. Susan told me how wonderful it had been to work with him over a period of many years; and I shared with her my own experience that Ben had always managed to find time to give advice to a young practitioner like me.

Susan realized she could refer Ben's emergency patients to my practice and expressed confidence that we would treat them well. Soon our office team was overwhelmed. We agreed that our goal was to deal with the current problems of these new patients and then return them to Ben. We provided the necessary care for their emergency needs and recommended they resume visits with Dr. Karp when he returned to the office. But it was not meant to be.

After a few weeks, I began to notice a pattern. Ben's patients all loved him. "He was more than my dentist; he was my *friend*," I heard repeated several times a day. Their comments reinforced my own understanding of the "secret" element in successful dentistry.

One morning, I awoke with a start at four o'clock. My heart pounded as I felt driven to express what I was feeling. I sat down at the desk in my study and took pen in hand. Magically, without contemplation or rewrite, the words flowed onto the page. I thanked Ben for the opportunity to continue for his patients his lifetime of providing quality dental care. I wrote that his patients valued him not only for his technical skill and caring manner but for that very special connection he was able to develop with people. He deeply understood the satisfaction we dentists get from meeting people, helping them, and becoming part of their lives. I quoted his patients' belief that he was their friend.

On my way to work that Friday morning, something told me I needed to deliver the letter right away; so I dropped it off at his home. I did not yet realize the importance of the timing of my action. Early the following Monday, I received a call from Mrs. Karp. She said that while visiting with Ben at the hospital Friday evening, she had read my letter to him. With a smile on his face and tears in his eyes, he squeezed her hand and whispered, "I guess I really did make a difference." Dr. Benjamin Karp died later that night.

Having told me of Ben's reaction to my letter, Mrs. Karp said she was also calling to ask that I read it at Ben's funeral. A few days later, as I walked to the front of the assembled mourners and looked at them from the podium, wave after wave of emotion engulfed me. Hundreds had gathered to pay homage to the memory of this wonderful man—a man whom so many had called their friend.

Today, I still treat many of Ben's former patients. They serve as a constant reminder never to postpone telling others words that can make them feel whole. As dentists, my colleagues and I understand that the mechanical aspect of our job is only one small part of what we can do for people.

Now and then, I reflect on the passing of Dr. Benjamin Karp and the occasion of my writing that letter. I ask myself what Force awakened me before sunrise on that day. What Power created those words that helped bring peace to a dying man and solace to his mourning widow? Had I waited another day to drop off the letter, my words would have fallen on newly deafened ears. Clearly, there is never a wrong time to tell people how much we care about them. If we don't act, those chances slip from our grasp and are lost forever.

Oscar Goren, DMD

"*I had a lovely birthday—my dentist sent me a card.*"

Body and Soul

As part of my early practice, my assistant and I started bringing our instruments and energy straight to a nearby nursing home in an effort to offer dental care to people who could not travel. A resident there named Judith was one of my first patients. An Italian lady who missed the spicy, fragrant foods of her home country, she politely tolerated the kitchen's attempts at pasta. While she had many problems with her teeth and always tried her best to follow the dentist's orders, eating with a knife and fork was especially troublesome for Judith since arthritis had gnarled her fingers.

I attempted simply to maintain Judith's dental condition so that she could eat, smile, and continue to use the dentures she had. Any major change would have been drastic for her physical and psychological wellbeing. Each visit with her required a cleaning with fluoride, or an exam, or the tightening of her denture. As the years passed, it was inevitable that Judith's weight dwindled, but her smile *never* faded.

One day I received a phone message from a nurse at the home indicating that Judith was again complaining about her teeth. I had seen this patient twice in the previous week and was beginning to wonder if I had to refer her to an outside facility for x-rays.

As I greeted Judith, she responded with a big hello and a quick, jerky tightening of her twisted fingers on my arm. On this visit, she was vague about which area of her mouth was causing trouble although her quick eyes followed my every movement. Slowly, an idea dawned on me. I leaned over and looked directly into her eyes. "Judith," I said slowly, "I promise to stop by and say hello to you every week when I come to treat the other residents." Immediately, Judith's eyes brightened and her smile widened. "Would you like that?" I asked.

"Would I ever!" was her reply.

As I continued my examination, I discovered that her symptoms had magically disappeared. Her teeth felt fine, her denture was fine, *life* was fine. As my assistant wheeled our patient out of the treatment room, Judith reminded her of my promise. My assistant's smiling eyes met mine over our masks.

One of the secrets of successful dentistry was revealed to us that day by a sweet lady's miraculous recovery. Sometimes the body will present us with a toothache that must be treated immediately and effectively. Sometimes the soul will present us with a need that must be treated with gentleness and compassion. And sometimes in dentistry, as in any other work, the body and the soul will present their needs in a complex blend of aching pains and earthy emotions that must be treated with wisdom, experience, and love.

Luz Abrera-Crum, DDS

Rainbow Child

*E*mpathy is your pain I feel in my heart.

Hospice Volunteer

Melissa is one of my best friends, and her mother was dying of cancer. I had tried repeatedly to reach Melissa by phone without success, and all I could do to provide emotional support was leave messages on her answering machine. One afternoon, as I was in the middle of a teeth-cleaning procedure, Melissa called me at the dental office. I apologized to my patient for the interruption and excused myself to take the call. I learned that my friend's mother had taken a serious turn for the worse and did not have long to live. Melissa apologized for not returning my calls earlier and kept the conversation brief by letting me know she was holding up all right. I told her I loved her and would talk with her again very soon.

I wiped the tears from my eyes and quickly returned to my patient whose four-year-old daughter sat busily coloring in the corner. My patient sensed the obvious change in my mood and inquired if I was all right. Trying hard not to tear up again, I quickly explained that my friend's mother was dying and tried cleverly to redirect attention to her with the dreaded, "Are you flossing?" question. My plan obviously succeeded, as she spent the next half-hour explaining the reasons for her dental neglect. While we spoke, her daughter continued to sit quietly in the corner with her gigantic box of Crayolas.

The appointment finally ended and I said goodbye to my patient. I then bent down to give her daughter a hug as I do with all the children who visit my office. With a smile on her face, the child handed me a folded sheet of paper. I opened it and saw the most beautiful rainbow I had ever seen in my life.

"Thank you," I said, "I'll hang it right here on my wall for everyone to see."

"No," she politely whispered, "this rainbow is not for you. It's for your friend's mommy."

Diane Stefanowicz, RDH

Mrs. Jackson

The way to love anything is to realize that it might be lost.

G. K. Chesterton

My early morning telephone conversation with Mom was a bad start to the workday. I stewed over it as I drove along Redwood Highway into the rural town of Cave Junction where I worked as a dental hygienist. "It was a mistake for you to move to such a remote location. You and Dave gave up such good paying jobs." Mom never understood our desire to leave the hustle and bustle of San Francisco for the slower, saner pace of Southern Oregon. Some things can't be measured in monetary value—like the sight of the sun breaking over a ridge of the Siskiyou Mountains.

"You have to drive so far to get to that rinky-dink office. What if you have an accident on those twisting country roads?" My mother was a strong-willed, outspoken woman. Widowed for more than twenty years, she was used to offering unsolicited opinions. But I knew that she always had my best interest at heart. I reminded myself that her criticism came out of love and concern. Nevertheless, that morning I was glad to be living 400 miles away from her. The distance buffered the friction between us.

I pulled into the parking lot of the cinder block building that housed the office of Dr. Joe Peters and went to work. The dentist's practice was eclectic. That's what I loved about working there—no two days were ever the same. We served patients of all ages, backgrounds, and persuasions. Some were fifth generation Oregonians and others were recently transplanted Californians, like me. All were friendly.

On this particular day, the schedule was hectic. It was mid-July, and the small office had grown quite warm by afternoon. The oscillating fan in my operatory was working at full speed. My 3:00 PM patient, Mrs. Jackson, was new to the practice. At 76, she was quite frail so her daughter had brought her in to have her teeth cleaned and examined.

I greeted my patient and led her into the operatory. She moved slowly, easing herself into the dental chair with a great sigh. I positioned the fan to allow her as much cooling relief as possible. Then I pulled up my operator's stool and sat down to review her health history form with her.

"I see you're taking Coumadin, Mrs. Jackson."

"Oh, yes. The doctor has me on it because of my blood pressure. I had a stroke a year ago. I guess he's afraid I'll have another."

I explained that Coumadin is an anticoagulant and that there was a chance she would experience excessive bleeding during the cleaning. I told her that I needed to consult her physician to determine whether I could safely clean her teeth that afternoon. Mrs. Jackson understood my concern and excused me while I telephoned her physician's office. I left a message with the nurse and returned to my patient. I checked her blood pressure while we waited.

Mrs. Jackson apologized for the delay she presented. "You must be awfully busy, and here I've held up your schedule."

"Not at all. It's important for us to have your physician's clearance before we treat you."

"Well, leave it to me to throw a monkey wrench in the works. Seems like it's all I'm good for anymore. Ever since I had that stroke, I've been unable to do so many things for myself. My daughter, Phyllis, has to drive me everywhere. I don't know how I'd manage without her." Tiny beads of perspiration ringed Mrs. Jackson's pale face, and her blue eyes clouded with sadness. "My husband died two years ago. I miss him so much."

"How long were you married?" I asked.

"Fifty years."

"Fifty! A lifetime," I marveled.

"Yes, it certainly was," Mrs. Jackson nodded. "I'm so lost without him now. And I'm no use to anyone like this. I wish the Lord would just take me." She closed her eyes and leaned back against the headrest. The fan gently blew the white hair from her damp brow.

Her soft-spoken words tugged at my heart. *There could be my own mother, some years from now*, I thought.

Mrs. Jackson's physician responded to our call promptly. Yes, he did require that she go off of the Coumadin for several days prior to any dental procedures. We had to reschedule her appointment. At the front desk, I informed Phyllis of the situation.

"Oh, Phyllis, now you have to make another trip to bring me back," Mrs. Jackson fretted.

"Don't you think anything of it, Mama. That's what I'm here for." I watched as Phyllis took Mrs. Jackson by the arm and carefully led her out to the car.

That evening when I got home, I called my mother. She was surprised to hear from me. (Two conversations in one day!)

"You know, Mom, I was realizing today that you'll be retiring soon. You really ought to think about moving up here to Oregon. I know it's quiet and out-of-the-way, but it's a great place to live. If you spend some time visiting here, you might find you'd really like it. Besides...we'd be close to each other."

That was more than twelve years ago. Since then my mother did indeed move to Oregon where she has watched her two grandsons grow up. Together, we have been a constant source of love, help, and companionship to each other.

Thank you, Mrs. Jackson. I'll never forget you.

Katharine A. Simmons, RDH

Johnny

There is no difficulty that enough love will not conquer.

Emmet Fox

"Johnny, where are we?" a frightened voice asked in Room 1. My stomach twinged, my head pounded, and my back ached from a day of contorted twists around the dental chair. How could dental school possibly have prepared me for the rigors of dentistry—a profession requiring the deftness of a surgeon, the temperament of a psychologist, and the stamina of a marathoner?

"Hello, I'm Dr. Gerstner." I was surprised to see an old woman in a pink flowered dress with gray hair neatly combed and held in place with a pink barrette. Her lined and wrinkled face contrasted with the childlike stare in her eyes.

"Hello, Doctor, I'm Johnny Mills," a man said introducing himself. "This is my wife, Mary." Mills released his wife's hand to shake mine with a strong, forceful grip a man of 70 is not supposed to have.

The woman cried out, "Johnny?"

"I'm right here, Dear." Mills patted her hand.

"How can I help you?" I asked; then forced a smile.

"My wife has a tooth that's cutting her tongue."

I slipped on a pair of rubber gloves for the examination and then checked Mary's medical history. She was in perfect health except for Alzheimer's disease.

Mr. Mills moved to the left side of the chair out of my way and let go of Mary's hand for a moment. Agitated, she demanded, "Johnny?"

I attempted to look inside Mary's mouth with a small mirror, but her loud scream of "No!" forced me to drop it on the floor in my haste to remove it. A second, stronger spasm struck my stomach.

"I'm sorry, Doctor. Mary, you have to let the doctor look in your mouth." Mr. Mills remained calm.

"Johnny, take me home!"

"Doctor, please try again," her husband urged.

Braced for a second round, I unwrapped a new mirror, then used gentle force to open her mouth.

"I brush and floss her teeth twice a day."

"I can tell; they look great, but she has a chipped filling."

"Can you fix it?"

"If she lets me."

Mills smiled, "She will."

Mary tried to pick up an instrument, but her husband stopped her saying, "Leave it alone, Dear."

Again, she said, "Johnny?"

I opened her mouth for another peek and saw there was no decay on the tooth. A fast pass with the drill to smooth the edge should do it. But when I tried, Mary kicked the bracket tray so that the instruments flew into the air and then crashed to the floor.

"Johnny, take me home!"

Mills' face was red with embarrassment. "I'm sorry."

My temples pounded and my stomach churned. "Mr. Mills, I don't believe this will work; your wife needs to be sedated."

"Please, Doctor, I'll control her."

"I don't know...."

"Please."

The heartfelt way Mr. Mills said it convinced me to try once more. I attempted to open his wife's mouth with a new mirror, but she resisted. This forced me to look at Mr. Mills as if to say, "See?"

"Let me try something." Then Mills began to sing in his wife's ear. He sang softly, without music, but it still sounded great.

Mary's face brightened and she said, "My Johnny!" Mills continued his serenade for several minutes until Mary fell asleep; apparently the stress she was feeling had exhausted her.

"Try now."

I opened her mouth and Mary didn't move, so I inserted a prop to keep it that way. As I smoothed the tooth, I held my breath. When the procedure was done, I almost let out a cheer.

"Thank you, Doctor. I really appreciate your patience."

"Mr. Mills.... The song...? Never mind, it's none of my business."

"I sang it at a wedding where Mary and I first met. The bride requested that song for her first dance with the groom. Mary told me she fell in love with me right then and there."

"You married after that?"

Mr. Mills nodded, "Fifty years ago. Some in my family think I should place her in a home, but I can't. I'll care for her as long as I can."

"You're doing a wonderful job," I said, summing up my thoughts perfectly. The sharp pain in my head and stomach began to ease.

When I removed the napkin from around Mary's neck, she opened her eyes, smiled at me, and asked, "Where's Johnny? I want to go home."

Danny Gerstner, DDS

Christmas Roses

When you carry out acts of kindness, you get a wonderful feeling inside. It is as though something inside your body responds and says, "Yes, this is how I ought to feel."

Rabbi Harold Kushner

It was the afternoon of December 24, the day before Christmas; and as the newest hygienist in our office, I had to work. The only thing that brightened my day was the beautifully decorated Christmas tree in our waiting room and a gift sent to me by a fellow I was dating—a dozen long-stemmed red roses.

As I was cleaning my operatory, our receptionist came and said there was a lady in the front office that urgently needed to speak with me. As I stepped out, I noticed a young, tired-looking woman with an infant in her arms. Nervously, she explained that her husband—a prisoner in a nearby correctional facility—was my next patient. The guards were scheduled to bring him to the office that afternoon. She told me she wasn't allowed to visit her husband in prison and that he had never seen his son. Her plea was for me to let the boy's father sit in the waiting room with her as long as possible before I called him for his appointment. Since my schedule wasn't full, I agreed. After all, it *was* Christmas Eve.

A short time later, her husband arrived—with shackles on his feet, cuffs on his hands, and two armed guards as an escort. The woman's tired face lit up like our little Christmas tree when her husband took a seat beside her. I kept peeking out to watch them laugh, cry, and share their child.

After almost an hour, I called the prisoner back to the operatory. While I worked, the guards stood just outside my door. The patient seemed like a gentle and humble man. I wondered what he possibly could have done to be held under such conditions. I tried to make him as comfortable as possible.

At the end of the appointment, I wished him a Merry Christmas—a difficult thing to say to a man headed back to prison. He smiled and thanked me. He also said he felt saddened by the fact he hadn't been able to get his wife anything for Christmas. On hearing this, I was inspired with a wonderful idea.

I'll never forget the look on both their faces as the prisoner gave his wife the beautiful, long-stemmed roses. I'm not sure who experienced the most joy—the husband in giving, the wife in receiving, or myself in having the opportunity to share in this special moment.

Lenora P. Rutledge, RDH

2

TRANSFORMATIONS

Be true to your teeth or they'll be false to you!

Author Unknown

Lola's Nose

I have seen women of 70 and older in deep depression, almost a catatonic depression that nobody could seem to get them out of, until somebody thought of taking them to a beauty parlor.

Carlfred Broderick

After graduating from the University of Maryland dental school, I accepted a one-year internship at Sea View Hospital in New York. Once a prominent facility in the treatment of tuberculosis, Sea View had become little more than a home for senior citizens unable to care for themselves due to chronic illness or financial hardship. As a young practitioner interested in all phases of dentistry, I found myself challenged with every sort of advanced adult dental treatment. Illness, neglect, old age, and lack of financial resources had conspired to turn routine problems into the most difficult challenges I would face in a 30-year dental career.

One day Lola, age 81, was wheeled in to the dental clinic. (Many of our patients were in wheelchairs or flat on their backs on stretchers.) Something about Lola was different, however.

While many of our patients were sad or chronically depressed, Lola wasn't even *there*. Her eyes were vacant—sort of unfocused—seemingly not even connected to a brain. Except for the gauze wrapped around her head making a horizontal bandana across her nose, her face was blankly attractive. But there seemed to be some sort of elegant humanity there…somewhere…silently behind the surface. Or so it seemed to me—based on exactly what, I couldn't tell you.

I introduced myself cautiously and promptly learned that she had no interest in being in the clinic and was only there because the nurse brought her. I asked if she had any dental problems. She said there was nothing in particular. This minimal exchange of conversation was accomplished on her part with a very few barely audible words…and no emotion. She passively permitted me to look in her mouth.

Lola had dentures that were so loose and ill fitting as to be almost useless. This was largely due to the fact that a large part of her upper jaw—the front part of the palate—was missing. Cancer surgery had produced a grossly deformed anatomy. Suddenly I understood what the facial bandage was about. Intellectually, I realized immediately that she had had facial surgery she was trying to keep from view. But in my mind's eye, I was still seeing the woman with her missing parts essentially filled in. Sort of like how, when we see an almost closed "C," our brain tends to fill in the missing part and we identify it as an "0" or a "circle." But then I found myself in touch with the fact that she was living with what would be a gross deformity for just about anyone.

With that realization, I sat back and just talked quietly with Lola. I told her I felt I could understand that it must be hard for her. I explained that sometimes dentists made facial prostheses—artificial facial parts made out of rubber or plastic—worn with a temporary adhesive to fill in and esthetically replace missing parts. Sometimes people lose an ear, a nose, or an eye along with part of the cheek structure or other part of their face as a result of a car accident or other trauma—or due to cancer surgery for the removal of diseased tissue. I told her I didn't know very much about making prostheses, but that it was something I was interested in learning. I suggested that if she wanted me to, I'd try to make a prosthetic nose for her so she would look pretty much normal.

I started to get excited about making a facial prosthesis, something only very few dentists ever have the opportunity to do. Lola's response was a blank. I couldn't tell if she had heard me at all. I thought she should be jumping out of her wheelchair; but no, she barely responded at all. I kept talking—at this point, more for me than for her. Eventually, she minimally indicated that *if I wanted to do it, she would go along*. Well, that was a good enough reason for me!

Over the next month or so, I spent several days at a cancer hospital in Brooklyn where it was routine practice to make facial and other prostheses for patients. The doctors and dentists there were generous in sharing information and techniques that I could take back to Sea View. During that period and after, I saw Lola several times in the clinic to get impressions—molds—of her mouth and also of her entire face. From these, I made plaster models of her face and her mouth.

As the visits passed, Lola began to get used to me and tolerated my probings and stretchings and the drippy, sticky, sometimes slimy, materials. Gradually, she came to see our meetings as a social event and began to talk more. She was okay being there with me *face to face* with her bandages off and part of her face missing. Eventually, she even demonstrated a little spark of excitement.

I came to understand that Lola didn't want to allow herself to get her hopes up of looking normal again for fear of being let down...again. I also came to understand that when patients lose body parts like legs or arms, usually their family still comes to visit. But when someone loses part of their face, I painfully learned, it was not at all uncommon that family and friends stop coming altogether. I'm sure nobody *intends* to stop, it just seems they lose their ability to *relate* to the patient. It's as if so much of our identity is tied up in our *faces* that when the face is destroyed, so is the identity. This sad fact has been reported often in medical journals by other professionals who work regularly with such patients.

Over the next months, I managed to fashion a silicone rubber prosthetic nose for Lola that closely matched her skin texture and color. Unless you knew what to look for, you'd never have guessed it was not part of her! Between that—and a new set of dentures—she looked, as Billy Crystal might say, *Ab-so-lute-ly Mah-vel-ous!* Lola was actually in tears of happiness the first time I fitted her with the prosthesis.

I dismissed her from treatment with the caution not to put makeup on the prosthesis as it was not skin and could possibly be damaged. She laughed...the thought of using makeup was so alien to her that she considered my caution ridiculous.

Prior to this, Lola never left her wheelchair except for her bed; and she never spoke to anybody. She just sat day after day in her ward staring vacantly into space.

About a month after finishing her treatment, I went to her ward to see how she was doing. Lola was nowhere to be found. I learned from a nurse that Lola had become the self-appointed social director for her ward and others. Though 81 years of age, she no longer used her wheelchair at all and constantly flitted about here and there under her own power.

When I finally caught up with Lola, I was tempted to yell at her—but stopped myself in time. She was using makeup all over her face for the first time in years and had almost ruined the prosthesis. But she was *alive*! She had come alive again not only physically, but emotionally as well. I can't describe how good I felt to have been a part of turning that caterpillar into the butterfly before me!

I don't know how much longer Lola lived. I had to leave Sea View and serve two years in the Army. But I always feel good knowing that as long as she did live, she was *really alive*. Sometimes I call on the memory of Lola to help me put my own troubles in perspective. All her dormant spirit needed was a little bit of love to wake up and fly once again.

Hi, Lola, wherever you are!

Michael C. Goldman, DDS

More Than Skin Deep

As is our confidence, so is our capacity.

William Hazlitt

Cassie was a quiet, demure girl. If you were unkind, you might have called her "mousy." She had no qualities that made her stand out from any other teenager. Her hair was not quite blond. Her eyes were blue—probably pretty if you could have seen them—but they were always downcast. Her features were regular—another way of saying "ordinary." She rarely smiled. When Cassie did smile, she covered her mouth with her hand. Although she was youthfully slender, this girl carried herself as though ashamed of her appearance.

Her mother, by contrast, was a vivacious, outgoing woman. Cassie's passive withdrawal saddened and frustrated her mother. "I graduated from Vassar," the parent confided. "Cassie could, too. That girl is my legacy, and she's more than bright enough in her own right. But she won't even try." Eyes glistening, Cassie's mother shook her head and said, "She wants to join the Peace Corps and go off somewhere to teach people how to plant potatoes. It's almost as if my daughter is running away."

The situation was sad, of course, but children often disappoint their parents. This particular disappointment seemed inevitable. Cassie just didn't appear to have the right stuff. *For this girl,* I thought to myself at the time, *taking the easy road might be the smart course. Maybe she alone knows what is best for herself.*

At one of her regular checkups, Cassie shyly voiced concern about the appearance of her front teeth. "Could they be capped?" she asked. Her "centrals"—the dental profession's term for the four front teeth—were small and had gaps between them. But they were sound.

"Don't be silly," I told her. "There's nothing wrong with your front teeth. They look fine to me. And they're perfectly healthy. There's no reason to cap them. Just forget about it."

Cassie and I had the same conversation on her next checkup. This time, she managed to blurt out that she thought they could "look better." But again, my surgeon's judgment prevailed.

Another six months later, I repeated my dismissal of Cassie's concerns about her front teeth. But this time she firmly indicated her commitment to having them capped. Since she thought I didn't want to do the job, she asked if I would refer her to another—more accommodating—dentist. Finally recognizing just how determined the girl was, I agreed to do the job. Once the procedure was completed, I had to admit that her newly capped front teeth looked quite nice.

On a clear, sunny afternoon about four months later, Cassie's mother walked into my office unannounced. Confronting me in the hallway, she said, "Excuse me, Doctor. Do you have a minute? I want you to see what you've done to Cassie."

My blood ran cold. What this woman had just said was terrifying. In that instant, I didn't know if I was facing retribution, a malpractice lawsuit, or both. I couldn't decide which of the two fates would be worse. But I managed to force a weak smile and croaked "Sure" as I followed her out to my waiting room.

There, walking toward me with perfect grace, was a beautiful young woman with sparkling eyes. It took me an astonished moment to recognize my visitor. This was not the mousy Cassie I had known. This Cassie was bright and outgoing—a lovely, confident girl.

"I wanted to thank you for my new look," she said, flashing a dazzling smile, "before I leave for Vassar."

"Vassar?"

"Yes," Cassie's mother said, arm held tightly around her daughter's shoulders and relishing the moment. "Cassie's going to be a freshman this fall." At last, the vivacious woman and the vivacious girl truly looked like mother and daughter.

Cassie smiled at her mother and nodded. "I decided I could be a much bigger help to the Peace Corps after I finish my education."

Cassie later graduated from Vassar College and moved on with her life. I never saw her again. But I've never forgotten the lesson she taught me. When this young woman believed that—because of her teeth—she wasn't pretty, she was right. She wasn't. I had corrected Cassie's problem without even recognizing one had existed. While *I* hadn't thought she had a problem, *Cassie* did. And no matter how much of an expert *I* was, it was *Cassie's* opinion of herself that mattered—not mine.

In the 1860's, Dr. Joseph Lister taught his young students: "Listen to your patient. He is trying to tell you what is wrong with him." It's still a fundamental lesson that each and every doctor—including us surgeons—has to learn. For some, we have to *relearn* it.

Jay L. Wolff, DDS

"Cosmetic dentistry changed my life."

Annie's New Smile

Once upon a time, I was beautiful. My hair was thick and dark and glossy...my skin was smooth and soft as a ripe peach...my mouth was dark pink...my eyes were large and clear.... Unfortunately, I was four years old at the time. It's been downhill ever since.

Geneen Roth

When I first met Annie I could sense there was something deeply wrong. She was a very pleasant woman with a calm and caring demeanor, and it was always a pleasure to see her. Nevertheless, there seemed to be some underlying signs of imbalance.

To begin with, her oral hygiene was almost non-existent. When I asked Annie how long it had been since she last saw a dentist she replied, "About three decades." As could be expected, I informed her that she needed a considerable amount of dental work. She didn't seem to mind and was anxious to embark on an extensive treatment plan to improve her condition. With a twinkle in her eye, I remember her saying, "When can we get started?"

I began to treat Annie. She always showed up for appointments promptly and remained courteous and composed even after undergoing extended dental procedures. Now I prefer to maintain a professional distance from the patients I treat, but Annie was beginning to erode this barrier. Perhaps due to the fact that I needed to see her so frequently, we began to develop a comfortable doctor-patient relationship. Actually, we began to develop a *friendship*.

I came to learn that Annie had tragically suffered the loss of her son almost 30 years earlier. As the mother of a young boy myself, I could not imagine the pain she must have endured over the years. She admitted to me that she had lost the will to live. And then, as if the tragic loss of a child wasn't enough pain, Annie was diagnosed with cancer.

Chemotherapy had robbed Annie of the body's protective oral lubricants, and her teeth began to deteriorate. She lost all of her hair and her skin turned a jaundiced yellow. The doctors only gave her a ten percent chance of living, so she stopped paying attention to her appearance. Miraculously, though, she recovered from cancer. Her hair eventually grew back and her skin condition improved. But she could not recover from the loss of her son. So she never sought dental treatment. And besides, she said, "Nobody sees my teeth anyway."

In our conversations, Annie would always refer to me as Dr. Karnazes. But because we had grown so close I told her it was fine to use my first name, Julie. Still she felt uncomfortable calling me by my first name because I was a doctor. "You earned that degree," she said, "and I want to respect it."

"But it seems so formal," I replied.

"All right," said Annie, "then I'll call you Dr. Julie." We both had a chuckle at that.

Eventually, Annie's mouth started to look better. At the conclusion of each appointment, she would look in the mirror, lift her upper lip with her finger or pull down her chin and inspect her teeth. "Very nice, Dr. Julie," she would often say.

After a year of treatment, Annie's dental work was nearly completed. I still vividly recall that final day. She came to her appointment in a brand new dress; it was bright and cheerful. I got the feeling that this was more than just a final visit to the dentist, it was a time of healing.

At the conclusion of the appointment, I asked Annie if she would like to look in the mirror. She stood up, studied her reflection carefully, and then did something she had never done before. She slowly parted her lips, crinkled her eyes, and opened her mouth in a broad smile to expose a beautiful new set of gleaming white teeth.

She stared in the mirror, transfixed, for quite some time. And then, without notice, she broke down and began to cry. I walked over, placed my hands on her shoulders, and asked, "Annie, is everything okay? Are you not happy with the dental work?"

"Oh no," she replied, "the work you did is wonderful."

"Then what is the matter?"

Annie slowly raised her head, looked me squarely in the eyes, and with tears still streaming down her face, said, "Dr. Julie, this is the first time I've smiled in 28 years."

Julie Karnazes, DDS

The Gift

Expressed affection is the best of all methods to use when you want to light a glow in someone else's heart and feel it in your own.

Ruth Stafford Peale

I watched from the reception desk as my husband carefully leaned over to examine Mrs. Sheridan, an elderly lady whom I had just seated in the dental chair. At the time, I had been the office manager and dental assistant in our busy family practice for nearly 10 years. In that period, I had grown accustomed to seeing Dr. Jim perform frequent, random acts of kindness. For me, Mrs. Sheridan is one of the more memorable beneficiaries of his special talents.

Mrs. Sheridan's husband had died the previous year. Since then, it seemed as if she had just about given up on her own life. When she first arrived at our office, she resembled a bag lady. Short, layered in wrinkled clothing and wearing a babushka, she smelled like stale bread. The poor woman barely raised her eyes to look around and I could hardly notice her mouth move when she talked to me in an ever-so-soft voice.

My desk is located just a few yards from my husband's

operatory. As the weeks passed, I was able to observe Mrs. Sheridan's gradual transformation. I could hear her conversations with my husband as well. She told him all about not wanting to go out of the house and what an effort it had been to come to the dental office. She spoke lovingly of her late husband and cried when she told Dr. Jim how empty her life had become.

At the beginning of each of Mrs. Sheridan's visits, my husband would make sure she was comfortable, push back in his rolling chair, and listen attentively to her stories before ever starting to work. His relaxed and soothing manner never failed to put her at ease.

Mrs. Sheridan had soft teeth—osteoporosis, I guess—and they had begun to decay and break. You didn't have to look closely to see that the sharp edges had begun to cut small cracks into her lip line. "I know I've neglected myself," she whispered as she gazed up and smiled weakly at Dr. Jim. He patted her shoulder and continued to work.

Two months after the process began, Mrs. Sheridan came in for the last of her weekly appointments. I'll never forget seeing her enter the office that day carrying a small flowered bag. "Is he ready for me?" she asked with more energy than she had ever shown before.

"Why, yes M'am, he is. Come on in and I'll get you seated." I held her arm and walked the patient to the operatory. In her delicate and fragile way, Mrs. Sheridan eased into the chair, pulled her colorful bag tightly against her bosom, and arranged her black leather purse on her lap.

As Dr. Jim entered the doorway, Mrs. Sheridan twisted a little in the chair, held up the bright new bag, and said, "I've been shopping. Now I can put on this makeup when you're finished."

Dr. Jim grinned and said, "Why I see you have indeed. You can use my big mirror here in the hallway if you like." My husband then turned, winked at me, and pointed to his head. I quickly understood he was signaling me to notice Mrs. Sheridan's newly styled hair. What a surprise! She was like a new person—her hair neatly twisted in a bun freshly tucked at the collar with a small clip.

As Dr. Jim finished the procedure, Mrs. Sheridan's smile was like new again—her front teeth had been restored. Where a short time before there had been a montage of dark, broken teeth in various shapes and angles, there now stood two even rows of glistening white pearls. Her lips—once cut, bleeding, and crusted with tiny scabs—were now smooth and vital looking. Dr. Jim placed a small mirror in front of her on the dental tray so she could survey her new look. He then left the room to give her a bit of privacy.

Like a little girl, Mrs. Sheridan gleefully opened her flowered bag, removed a golden tube, and carefully applied a coat of red lipstick. Next, without bothering to get up from the chair, she dusted her face with pink powder. A dab of rouge on each of her cheekbones completed the change process.

With these final touches, I could see a brand new radiance infuse our patient. What I observed was a transformation far deeper than the results of my husband's fine dentistry or the enhancements of Estée Lauder cosmetics. Mrs. Sheridan was, quite simply, a brand new person. It was as if there was a light beaming from inside her that was far more noticeable than the outer changes that had taken place.

When our patient signaled she was ready to leave the office, I carefully lifted the arm of the chair and invited her to take a look in the big mirror in the hallway. As she did so, Dr. Jim rounded the corner from the lab. Mrs. Sheridan looked up, smiled at him and said, "I don't need a mirror to see how I'm feeling today. Why, I'm shining all over. I feel as though my soul is brand new and I'm ready to begin the rest of my life."

Dr. Jim held out his hand and, for a moment, Mrs. Sheridan

looked like an angel. She didn't return my husband's hand-shake; instead she took his hand between her own and pulled it to her face. "My son died three years ago. When I lost my husband last year, it seemed like the end of my world. I forgot who I was. Your kind words and gentle way of listening have helped me to find myself again. I am so grateful to you."

That afternoon when our day's work was over, Dr. Jim and I went home, knelt down together, and said a prayer of humble thanks for Mrs. Sheridan's gift to us.

MJ Endres

On the Edge of Maybe

Behind every tooth there is a person.

Author Unknown

I watched as an orderly wheeled Mr. Forest down to the dental ward from one of the Veteran's Administration Hospital floors. I waited for him in the hallway and introduced myself when he arrived. Explaining that I would be his dentist, I indicated I was going to perform a complete dental exam. My new patient acknowledged me with a grunt and a sideways glance while I stood in silence and studied him. Mr. Forest was a man in his thirties whose appearance was somewhat unkempt. His feet were bandaged and covered with large gray hospital slippers. Slumped in the wheelchair, he stared at the floor while moving about restlessly.

"I don't know why I have to come here. What do you want with me?" he demanded.

I replied, "You're scheduled for a dental exam because your doctor felt you needed dental treatment."

He shrugged. "I don't need any dental treatment."

I didn't feel it would benefit either of us if I continued with an unwanted exam. I decided to let him make the decision, thus giving him control of the situation. "It's up to you," I replied. "If you're not feeling well we can reschedule your appointment."

"No, just go ahead," he said in a resigned tone of voice.

Needless to say, we both felt less than enthusiastic about our initial encounter. I completed the exam. He had not had regular dental care and was missing his upper front teeth. He did not have any dentures or bridges to replace the teeth he had lost. I could tell he was self-conscious about his appearance, so I explained the recommended treatment of an upper denture and lower bridgework. During the course of our conversation he was non-committal and avoided eye contact. "There's a lot I could do for you to help you get your mouth healthy again," I said.

"I don't know. Do you really have to do all this work?" he asked.

I realized he was not convinced of the need to proceed with treatment. Finally I paused and asked, "Do you think I'm going to extract your teeth and not give you a replacement?"

"You got that right!" he said emphatically. This was his first positive response so far in our conversation. He did not believe I would follow through with the proposed treatment plan. I realized I needed to gain his trust in order to treat his case.

"Mr. Forest, " I said, "I'm here to help you. I want to try to help you get your mouth healthy and give you something to chew with, but you've got to work with me." He responded with a skeptical expression; but at least he made eye contact. I felt perhaps there was a chance we could accomplish something together.

During subsequent appointments with Mr. Forest, we began to develop rapport, and we made progress. He started to open up to me and share details of his background. A Vietnam veteran, he had been homeless for awhile. During one especially cold winter, he had suffered severe frostbite resulting in partial amputation of both of his feet—the reason he was being treated at the VA Hospital. He had no concrete plans for what he would do once he was discharged and seemed to have little interest in his future.

Over several appointments, I began to notice a change in Mr. Forest's disposition. His appearance improved. Initially he had been unkempt and had a sour demeanor. After awhile, though, he seemed to actually look forward to his appointments. The ward nurse reported that other patients on the floor were teasing him because he "primped" himself before coming for his dental visits, brushing his teeth and hair, and changing his clothes. He began to wheel himself down to his appointments, sat up straight in his wheelchair, and even made small talk with the dental assistant and receptionist. On several occasions, he actually *smiled*. The day finally came when his denture and bridges were delivered. To my satisfaction, they fit well and looked great. I brought one of the other dentists over to my cubicle to show off the final result.

"Wow," she exclaimed when she saw Mr. Forest smiling with his new teeth, "you look just like a movie star!"

I joined in, "Get me my sunglasses, his smile is too bright!"

Mr. Forest and I both beamed. "Aw shucks," he said, "you guys are something else." Mr. Forest tried to downplay our excitement, but I knew he was very proud of his new teeth and his new look. "Thank you," he said to me quietly, "Thanks for everything."

On his follow-up visit a week later, Mr. Forest told me he would be discharged from the hospital soon. "Where will you go when you leave? Any plans for the future?" I asked. He told me he had contacted a relative with whom he could stay until he had definite plans.

"I want to start working part-time if I can," he said optimistically. He was making plans and looking forward to a better future.

"I hope things work out for you," I said as I shook his hand.

A week later, I attempted to schedule Mr. Forest for another follow-up appointment. I was disappointed to learn that he had already been discharged from the hospital, and the case was closed. I wondered where the future would lead him. I wondered whether he would be able to find a purpose for his life or continue to straddle the line of homelessness and despair. All that remained for me was to remember him in my thoughts and prayers.

On Memorial Day several months later, I was watching the local news on television. The annual Memorial Day parade was being broadcast, and spectators were being interviewed. Bands played, veterans marched, and the crowd cheered. Suddenly, Mr. Forest's face flashed on the screen. He was sitting in a wheelchair in the front row of spectators lining the edge of the street. Waving a small American flag, he flashed a broad grin and displayed a toothy smile that only his dentist could know was artificial.

"That's my patient!" I exclaimed, pointing to the television. "That's Mr. Forest from the VA Hospital." I turned up the volume and listened attentively.

Amid the festivities, Mr. Forest told the roving news reporter that he was proud to be a veteran of the U.S. military. "I want to honor and remember other veterans," he said, adding, "This is a great country." He seemed to be happy and at peace with himself. I remembered the transformation I had seen during the course of his dental treatment. I sensed that he had begun to trust others, feel better about himself and his appearance, and develop a feeling of self worth. I knew there were many obstacles that still lay ahead for him, but I felt sure he was moving in a positive direction. I was proud of him, and hoped that in some small way I had played a role in his newest—and possibly biggest—journey yet towards wellness and renewal.

"Keep up that fighting spirit, Mr. Forest," I said to the television. It was a Memorial Day I will never forget, and I saluted him as his face faded from the screen.

Susan Paurazas, DDS, MHSA, MS

3

THE TOOTH FAIRY

"Hi, I'm the tooth fairy. Want to buy back some of your teeth?"

I Saw the Tooth Fairy

Every child loves to share the loss of a first tooth with anybody who will listen—especially a dental hygienist who helps to care for those teeth.

A little girl was having her teeth cleaned in my dental chair one day while her mother sat and watched. I was excited to see that my patient had lost her first tooth; it gave me a fun thing to talk about during the appointment.

I asked if the Tooth Fairy had come to visit after she lost her tooth. "Yes," my patient said, and told me she got a dollar since it was her first tooth. I made a big deal about the dollar, but she interrupted me to say that there was more. *"I know what the Tooth Fairy looks like,"* she announced in a very secretive voice.

Now, I've worked with kids for years; they never talk about what the Tooth Fairy *looks* like, they mainly talk about what she leaves them—*money.* So I was curious as to what the little girl was going to say. "Tell me what the Tooth Fairy looks like," I asked.

She appeared eager to tell me but said she could only *whisper* the answer. I leaned over and put my ear close to her mouth while she breathlessly shared her secret.

"The Tooth Fairy looks kinda like my mommy—only *naked*!"

Deborah Goldberg Polay, RDH

The Tooth Fairy's Sister

Adam and Eve had many advantages,
but the principal one was that they escaped teething.

Mark Twain in *Pudd'nhead Wilson*

Erma, a patient of mine, gets the credit for this idea; and I've passed it on to many grateful mothers who can attest to its effectiveness.

Erma had two daughters, separated in age by about three years. As the children grew older, the eldest started losing her baby teeth. Naturally, these events were faithfully followed by visits from the Tooth Fairy.

It wasn't long before the younger child became jealous of the Tooth Fairy's favoritism toward her older sibling. "Mamma, how come the Tooth Fairy never visits me? It's not fair," she pouted.

Now at the time, Erma was trying to wean her youngest child from her pacifier. Suddenly, the concerned mother realized her daughter's envy could be put to good use. "Honey, I've never told you about this before, but the Tooth Fairy has a sister named the Paci-Fairy. If you put your pacifier under your pillow tonight, I'll bet the Paci-Fairy will visit you just like the Tooth Fairy visits your sister."

The following morning, the youngster discovered a present under her pillow while the pacifier had magically disappeared. "Look, Mamma! Look! The Paci-Fairy gave me some money."

The contented child never asked for her pacifier again—ever.

Alan H. Gelbert, DDS, FAGD

Tricking the Tooth Fairy

We started seeing Daniel when he was a three-year-old. In our practice, we've always encouraged parents to bring their children in starting at about that age so the youngsters begin their lifetime dental program with a "good" experience.

By the time Daniel was in the first grade, we discovered that a number of his baby teeth had to be extracted to make room for the adult teeth pushing up from below. (For most people, baby teeth simply loosen up and "fall out.") Each time we pulled one of Daniel's teeth, we'd pack it in a little plastic "tooth chest" so he could put it under his pillow. On each succeeding visit, we'd always ask if the Tooth Fairy had been good to him. Invariably, he'd say something like, "Oh yes, I got a dollar."

One day, Daniel came in for a routine checkup. We determined that no additional baby teeth needed pulling just then. It was at this point that Daniel confessed he had recently tried to trick the Tooth Fairy. The boy's new puppy had lost a tooth, so Daniel placed it under his pillow with the expectation of soon making another deposit in his piggy bank.

"When I looked under my pillow the next morning," Daniel told us, "all I found was a bone!"

Diane Hill, CDA

DENNIS the MENACE

"WILL YOU WRITE A LETTER TO THE TOOTH FAIRY AND ASK FOR MY TOOTH BACK? I THINK I CAN GET A BETTER DEAL SOMEWHERE ELSE."

Speechless

A few years ago, I performed a routine oral examination on a five-year-old. While her teeth and gums were in fine condition—reflecting the obvious coaching of dedicated parents—I'll never forget that experience. And I'll always remember Kelly, the adorable little girl with blond curls and a pearl barrette decked out in a flowered print dress, short white socks, and black Mary Janes. A plastic Minnie Mouse bracelet adorned her wrist.

When I finished my exam, I asked the child if she had any questions. With her hands quietly folded in her lap, she nodded, looked up at me from the dental chair, and asked, "Doctor, can you take out all my teeth?"

Surprised, I asked, "Kelly, why would you want to do a thing like that? Your teeth are in perfect condition!" Her reply left me speechless. Nothing I learned in eight years of college had equipped me to deal with what she said next.

"I've heard there's a very rich person—called the Tooth Fairy—who gives little children money for their teeth," Kelly continued. She explained that her parents fought a lot about money and that her father would be moving out very soon—divorce. "I'm going to sell my teeth to the Tooth Fairy and give the money to my mommy and daddy so they can stay together."

Michael H. Halasz, DDS

Calling the Tooth Fairy

Many years ago, I worked as a dental assistant for a small general practice. Dr. Jacobs always had a soft spot in his heart for our young patients, especially when they needed to have a tooth extracted. Immediately after the procedure, the dentist would make each child more comfortable by placing an important call to the Tooth Fairy—within earshot of the patient and the accompanying parent. His finger firmly on the receiver, the doctor's telephone "conversation" would go something like this.

"Hello, Operator? This is Dr. Jacobs calling. I have an important person-to-person call to place to the Tooth Fairy. It's urgent. (Pause.) Uh-huh, uh-huh, I see. Well, no, Operator, I really can't call back later. I *understand* the Tooth Fairy is especially busy today, but I have Cathy Jones in my office. This is a *very* important call."

After more hemming and hawing—his finger still on the receiver—the dentist would say, "Okay, I'll hold a few more seconds, but please hurry. I can't wait long."

Following an extended pause, the "conversation" would resume. "Oh, finally! Am I speaking to the Tooth Fairy? This is Dr. Jacobs calling from Smalltown and I need you to visit an extra special patient of mine tonight. That's right. Extra special. Uh-huh, uh-huh. Well, I know you're very busy, but this is important. Cathy just had a tooth removed and I know she needs you to visit tonight. That's right, Cathy Jones at 1234 Any Street. You'll be there tonight? Yes, I understand you'll have to work overtime. Okay, thank you very much, Tooth Fairy. I appreciate it. Goodbye."

The dentist would then rinse off the tooth, wrap it in gauze, place it in a small plastic box, and give it to the awestruck child. Winking at the parent, he would dismiss the patient who soon forgot the extraction and practically floated home on a river of anticipation. The Tooth Fairy never missed a visit when this dentist placed that special person-to-person call.

Ellen Dietz, CDA, BS

Looking Out for Grandma

During the course of treatment for one of my four-year-old pediatric dental patients, an extraction was required. Following the procedure, I showed the boy the tooth that was removed and told him about the Tooth Fairy.

We placed the tooth in a brightly colored plastic container, and I told him to put it under his pillow that night. I went on to explain that the Tooth Fairy would remove the tooth and leave some money.

His eyes lit up. He looked at me and stated that his grandmother left her teeth in a glass on the stand next to her bed every night. He couldn't wait to tell her to leave them under her pillow so she could also get some money.

Lawrence Yanover, DDS, PhD

A Surprise Ending

A young patient of mine lost his first tooth and proudly showed it to everyone as if it was a piece of gold. His smile lit up my room as he pulled the tooth out of his pocket and revealed his treasure. His mom explained that in the last week he had shown it to his grandmother, his mom's hairdresser, the cashier at the grocery store, and the vet. But Johnny had not yet allowed anyone to touch his precious tooth. As the boy grinned, his mom proceeded to explain what had happened the previous week.

The night Johnny lost his tooth, his mother told him to put it underneath his pillow and the Tooth Fairy would bring him a dollar. Johnny was thrilled to hear this. He could hardly settle down long enough to fall asleep. It was like waiting for Santa Claus.

The next morning, Johnny awoke bright and early to find a crisp dollar bill under his pillow. But to his surprise, the tooth was gone. Tears streamed down the boy's face as he went into his mother's room to tell her what had happened. She explained that the Tooth Fairy took the tooth and replaced it with a dollar bill.

Without hesitation, Johnny left the room. He returned minutes later carrying his piggy bank. He said, "Mommy, if I put my piggy bank under my pillow tonight do you think the Tooth Fairy would bring me back my tooth?"

Michelle M, Powers, RDH

4

ON KINDNESS
AND CARING

I long to accomplish a great and noble task, but it is my chief duty to accomplish small tasks as if they were great and noble.

Helen Keller

Pass It On

The most important things in life aren't things.

Linda Ellerbee

While I was a student in dental school, and during my subsequent education in orthodontic school, my wife and I were raising three children. Not surprisingly, our budget was severely strained. As I pursued my studies, a kindly pediatrician named Dr. Donald Strominger took care of our children's medical needs free of charge—as well as the children of numerous other dental and medical students. During this period, one of our daughters was hospitalized for ten days—and it cost us nothing. In our case, this term of free care lasted more than five years.

When I graduated from orthodontic school, I went to tell Dr. Strominger goodbye and thank him for his generosity. I told him that as soon as I started to earn some money I wanted to pay him back for his services. He bristled a little and said sternly, "I didn't treat your children to have you pay me back; I did it because I knew you needed the help. If you want to pay me back, do the same for your patients when you find people in need."

Not long after I started my orthodontic practice, the father of one of my patients was killed on a camping trip with the scout troop for which he was the Scoutmaster. He left a widow with several young children to raise. When she came in with her child for their next appointment, I expressed my deepest sympathies. Then I remembered Dr. Strominger's example. It brought a lump to my throat and a wonderful feeling to my heart as I told her there would be no charge for taking care of her children's orthodontic needs.

About a year later when I removed her son's braces, she came in to thank me and explained that she and her children where raising chickens to help provide income for the family. She then presented me with a freshly dressed chicken she had raised herself. After she left, I was surprised to find I was over-whelmed with emotion. As I thought about it, I realized that the payment of one chicken for a yearlong orthodontic case made me feel better than any amount of money I might have received. Dr. Strominger's gift not only helped me during school; his example has also made me a happier person throughout my professional career.

Over the years, I've been blessed with the opportunity to treat a number of deserving patients free of charge. Inevitably, many of them have said that when they got back on their financial feet, they wanted to repay me. Each occasion has given me the opportunity to repeat the words of Dr. Strominger: "I didn't treat you or your children to have you pay me back; I did it because I knew you needed the help. If you want to pay me back, do the same for others when you find people in need."

Dennis J. Michaelson, DMD, MS

Show Me a Sign

Blessed are those who engage in lively conversation with the helplessly mute—for they shall be called dentists.

Ann Landers

As a general dentist in a private practice for more than a decade, I have treated several deaf patients...but none as special as 13-year-old Tyler. It was my desire to communicate one-on-one with him that prompted me to study American Sign Language (ASL). I started attending evening classes a few hours each week and quickly discovered that there was far more to ASL than simply finger spelling each word.

Not long after I enrolled in the class, I had an appointment with Tyler. This was my first opportunity to attempt direct communication with him by signing. Of course, if it hadn't been for his mother's help as an interpreter, my fumbling efforts would have been a disaster. You see Tyler is not only deaf, he also has other physical handicaps that severely limit his motor skills—including dexterity with his fingers. This makes it very difficult for someone like me, with my limited ASL abilities, to understand what he is signing.

When I first told Tyler I had started taking ASL classes, he was delighted. However, the day he returned approximately six months later for his next checkup was a day I will never forget and makes other days seem insignificant by comparison.

Tyler hurried into my office (hurried being a relative term with Tyler's physical limitations) and immediately asked—by signing, of course—if I was still studying ASL. I assured him I was and reminded him it was not the Evelyn Wood *speed* signing class and asked him to slow down so I could understand what he was trying to tell me.

Since he had come with other members of his family needing dental care that day, Tyler made it known he wanted to be seen first. His mother readily agreed and said the others would remain in the waiting room until Tyler was finished. She told me that if I needed her help again as an interpreter, I only had to ask. She really wanted Tyler and me to communicate one-on-one. I was a bit anxious but eager to try and felt that if Tyler was patient with me, we'd get along perfectly. I'm sure the little prayer I whispered didn't hurt either. The appointment went fine, and I completely lost track of time until my dental assistants courteously reminded me I did have other patients to see.

When I finished treating the rest of Tyler's family, I told his mother I wanted to say goodbye to her son who, by that time, was waiting in the reception area. As we all stood there, Tyler signed, "You will never know how much it means to someone like me that you would take time to learn how to communicate in my language. I am so grateful. You and I will always be great friends!"

Tyler's mom, tears streaming down her cheeks, asked if I understood what Tyler had signed. I assured her I did...that kind of message didn't need an interpreter.

Never before that moment...or since...have I felt so humbled. I continue to take weekly ASL classes and remind myself daily never to take for granted the gifts God has given me: speech, sight, mobility, good health…and especially hearing.

Gregory V. McGowan, DDS

Tears of Thanks

Freedom is not free.

Martin Luther King, Jr.

I stepped through the doorway of our reception room to call my next patient. While I have long since forgotten his name, I will never forget his face. He was a big, burly, dark-skinned man with pools of brown liquid for eyes. New to our office, he was there to have his teeth cleaned and a thorough examination.

It had been a while since his last dental visit, he explained as he settled into my operatory chair. After placing the pastel bib around his thick, muscular neck, I bent over to fasten the clasp. It was then that my eyes glanced downward and I noticed his large, embossed belt buckle that read, "Vietnam War Veteran—And Proud of It!"

I began the appointment by creating a chart for our new patient. Taking a medical history and recording the necessary personal data, I observed that he was married and had a nine-year-old son. He said his employer provided decent dental insurance and that he was in our office to start taking better care of his teeth.

I made a full set of x-rays and stepped into the darkroom for a moment to develop them. As I stood in the blackness, I couldn't help but think of the patient sitting in my chair. In the forefront of my mind was a discussion I had recently had with friends regarding the plight of our Vietnam veterans. I had told them about a particularly moving article I read in *National Geographic* regarding the building of the Vietnam War Memorial in Washington, D.C. The story told of the emotion that spilled over when veterans stood in awe before that black granite wall and further described some of the items that were left there in memory of fallen comrades. The memorial had become a place of healing—that generation's Wailing Wall. I remembered the difficulty I experienced in reading the article as my tears blurred the words. My friends and I each offered our own stories about men we knew who had fought over there and had been seriously and sadly affected.

Developed x-rays in hand, I returned to my patient. With a bit of trepidation, I told him I had noticed his belt buckle. He looked at me as though trying to discern if I was friend or foe. I told him of my recent conversation with friends. He appeared surprised; and I guessed this was due to our age difference since I was a generation younger. I began to tell him of the empathy my friends and I felt for the soldiers and how we agreed we could never fully understand the hell they had endured.

He replied that he had been left with haunting images and told me about the difficulties of readjusting. When he returned from Vietnam, he simply could not pick up his life where he had left it prior to being drafted.

Something at this point in our conversation made it comfortable for him to continue. Maybe it was my compassion. Or maybe it was because I was a complete stranger. He told me of nightmares, periods of questioning his sanity, and a brief, wild stint in Mexico when he was driven by a desperate need to escape the memories of that war.

He told me that the love of his wife and son—especially his son—were what kept him going. He said he had told his son about some of his experiences in Vietnam and found that revealing its horrors had helped to exorcise the demons. He explained that as his son grows older, he intends to continue telling him about the experience so the boy will better understand his father.

As my patient spoke, I couldn't help but notice that everything about him was gentle—his voice, the way he moved his hands, and those eyes—big, warm, and soft. It was hard for me to picture him fighting in the dense jungles of Southeast Asia. The more he talked, the harder it got for me to listen. Not because it was too harsh or difficult to bear, but because my heart was getting sad. I wanted to say something that would matter. In the time we shared, I had forgotten my patient was a stranger, a man there for a cleaning and a checkup. I realized the minutes meant for his appointment were ticking away, and I still had a service to provide. I simply looked into those dark brown eyes and told him thank you. Thank you for going. Thank you for fighting. And, most important of all, thank you for coming back. I really don't remember whose eyes spilled the tears first.

Susan Skipper, RDH

The Christmas Gift

Christmas Eve dinner is always a festive occasion. While visiting relatives in his hometown, a man had just finished dessert when he felt new and unusual discomfort in his mouth, as if a sliver of bone had lodged between his teeth. A quick consultation with the bathroom mirror revealed that a porcelain crown had become dislodged and sat askew against the gum line. To avoid further complications, he needed the prompt assistance of a dentist—on Christmas Eve.

Quickly, he realized that because of the holiday weekend, it would be three days before most dental offices reopened. Did that mean he'd have to subsist on a liquid diet—and put up with the prospect of steadily increasing discomfort—for three whole days? Dentists of family acquaintance were buzzed; but nobody was home.

Finally, a nearby hospital provided an after-hours referral. The on-call dentist, reached at his house, was receptive. When assured there was as yet no severe pain, the dentist had a request of his own. "I prepare one meal a year for my family," the doctor said, "and the night before Christmas is a tradition in our household. Would you allow me to wind things up here first;

and then we can meet at my office?"

Late that evening, the patient was pronounced rehabilitated. There had been an x-ray, the rattling of picks on a tray, a swabbing of antiseptic, the spreading of cement, and the just-right repositioning of an errant crown. The appreciative patient told the dentist he'd pay by check or a bill could be mailed. The jeans-clad doctor demurred. "I can't charge for emergency work on Christmas Eve," he said waving his surgical-gloved hand. "There is no fee."

The visitor was flabbergasted, "This would have cost at least a hundred bucks back East, even if I could find somebody over a holiday weekend. At least tell me the name of your favorite charity." Tuesday morning, the dentist got a call from his local Salvation Army headquarters indicating they had received a gift of $100 in the dentist's name.

This little story of goodwill, appreciation, and generosity that typifies the Christmas spirit has a further seasonal sweetener. Yes, there truly is a Santa, for this dentist's name is Dr. David W. Clause.

Ken Berg, Retired Editor, The [Mankato, Minnesota] Free Press
Submitted by Carolyn K. Clause

House Calls

Like most dentists, I see quite a few patients in my office every week. As a result, I don't often make house calls—there just isn't time. Last December, however, I made an exception.

A woman phoned from a rural area twenty miles away and asked if I could come look at her elderly, homebound mother who had cracked a tooth. I was told the patient had Alzheimer's disease and could be moved only with great difficulty. I was also aware that advanced Alzheimer's sufferers should remain in familiar surroundings to avoid disorientation—and maybe even panic. In short order, I packed my field kit and headed down the highway.

Twenty miles and 45 minutes later, I arrived at my destination—a little house set in a grove of Arizona mesquite. The patient's daughter then explained the problem in more detail. It seems mom was in the habit of gnashing her teeth and had broken a "biting tip" off one of her lower molars. As the patient sat on the couch, I fitted a stainless steel crown over the cracked enamel. While my treatment wasn't fancy, the family was grateful and wrote me a nice note afterwards.

The following August, the daughter called again. Mom had

broken another tooth. Once more, I packed my field kit and headed for the little house. When I arrived, three puppies bounded up to the door and licked my shoes in greeting. This time, two other daughters were also present, visiting from California and Washington for their father's 85th birthday. The old man was seated on the couch with his arm around the patient—his wife—and asked me, "Are you here to see my sweetheart?"

Mom sat stiffly on the couch, in much the same position as I had left her in December. I pulled on my gloves and inspected her mouth. Everything seemed to be in order. "Where's the broken tooth?" I asked.

The daughter who had called handed me a fragment of enamel. "We found this at her feet," she explained. I peered down at the little white chunk but didn't say anything. "That is a tooth, isn't it?" she asked, anxious at my silence.

"Yes, it's a tooth, all right," I said slowly. "It's just not a *human* tooth."

"What!" the daughters exclaimed together.

I smiled. "It looks like a small dog's tooth. Your mom is fine."

There was a moment of silence followed by peals of laughter. Even the puppies started yapping and joined in the merriment.

I drove away amid a chorus of embarrassed thank you's. The daughters had been afraid I'd be angry. To my surprise, I felt pleased.

Although the clinical, problem-solving part of me knew the trip had not been productive, I realized that to my patient's family, their beloved mother had been well cared for. I fingered the puppy tooth. It was an unusual reminder of a well-worn truth that needs the periodic reinforcement I got that day: Dentistry is not just about procedures; it's about *people*.

Eric K. Curtis, DDS, MAGD

The Stolen Bicycle

About nine years ago, I read a story in the paper about a little boy named Jeremy whose bicycle had been stolen. It wasn't just any old set of wheels; it was a brand new bike that the boy had bought after saving money he made from working a paper route. It had taken him over a year to save up enough to buy the bike. Ten-year-old Jeremy was emotionally crushed. He couldn't believe that something this tragic could happen to him. The paper went on to say that it was setting up a fund to accept donations to buy the boy another bike.

As I read the article, something inside me identified with Jeremy. You see when I was a little kid, my bicycle had been stolen and I never got it back. At the time, I was heartbroken. Reading Jeremy's story brought me back to one of the worst experiences of my own childhood and I wanted to do something about it. Not just for Jeremy, but for me too! Deep down inside, I believed I could finally heal my own still-raw childhood wound by helping this boy.

I called Jeremy's home and spoke with his mother whose name I learned was Kathleen. I asked what type of bicycle had been stolen and where it was purchased. Loaded with this information, I went to the store and bought Jeremy a brand new bike—the same model, style, and color as the one that had been stolen. I then personally delivered it to his home. I did this without telling anyone what I was going to do—not Jeremy, not his mother, not my dental team, not even my wife. I just did it. For me, it was the right thing to do.

The expression on Jeremy's face when he saw the bike was all the thanks I needed. His mother was *so* thankful. Ecstatic, Jeremy immediately hopped on the bike and began riding up and down the sidewalk. I assured his mother I didn't want anything in return. She asked me who I was and I told her. Then I left. About a week later, I received a nice thank you note in the mail and that was the end of the matter...until last Wednesday. Last Wednesday, and nine years later, that is!

I was monitoring one of the courses at the Connecticut State Dental Association's annual meeting. The room was packed. In fact it was overflowing into the hallway and beyond to the poolside area of the hotel. As I made arrangements for more chairs, a woman approached and asked if I was Dr. Maroon. "Yes," I said, "what can I do for you?"

She answered, "You probably don't remember me, but about nine years ago you bought a bicycle for my son, Jeremy."

"Yes, I do remember you...your name is Kathleen," I responded as I refreshed my memory by glancing at her nametag.

She continued, "Well, I was hoping to see you here so I could thank you again for all you've done for my family. The bike has been handed down to three kids and they've all loved it. After you told me you were a dentist, I got to thinking about my life and realized I wasn't happy in my job. I decided to change careers and have become a dental hygienist. I graduated a couple of years ago and am very happy. Jeremy is now in college taking pre-dental courses and hopes to be a dentist someday. That one experience has made such an impact on our lives that I wanted to let you know!"

I was dumbfounded and couldn't think of anything bright to say. Instead, I just mumbled, "Thanks.... I'm so happy for you all."

After we parted company, I had to sit down. I couldn't believe what had just happened. How, nine years earlier, could I have predicted something like that? How many lives did I affect with that one tiny little action? Think about it! How many people will Kathleen come in contact with as a hygienist during her career? Probably thousands. How many people will Jeremy come in contact with as a dentist during his career? More thousands! How many people will they help during their lives? You tell me! And how many of the people they help will go on to help others...and so on? It boggles the mind. The power of giving is simply awesome...and humbling. Isn't life wonderful? Isn't it great to be alive? You bet it is! Just ask me!

Michael Maroon, DMD, FAGD
Submitted by Peter P. Mullen, DDS

Solace

There is no exercise better for the heart than reaching down and lifting people up.

John Holmes

Caron was a 46-year-old recovering heroin addict when she was first introduced to me in my final year of dental school. As a fourth-year student, I had the luxury of treating patients in my own cubicle with the supervision of faculty. Due to her glazed eyes and expressionless face, Caron was often referred to as a "space cadet." She was definitely "out there" most of the time. On those occasions when I provided treatment for her, I invariably had difficulty in securing an instructor to supervise my work. Everyone from peers to faculty avoided me like the plague when Caron was in my chair.

The years of homelessness and heroin addiction had ravaged Caron's body. She was an encyclopedia of immunocompromised diseases ranging from diabetes to Hepatitis C—to name a few. In recent years, her vice had turned from heroin to nicotine. She coughed constantly and freely sprayed the atmosphere with droplets of her saliva throughout every procedure.

She complained as soon as she got into the dental chair: "It's too hot!" "It's too cold!" "Ain't we done yet?" These were among her favorite utterances that would be repeated 30 to 40 times during every visit. It would be an understatement to say that Caron was a difficult patient.

Oftentimes, I used the same techniques on Caron that I found useful when working with my pediatric patients—for she was childlike in many ways. She would pick up my dental instruments and play with them as soon as I left the chair to get her x-rays. But somehow, for some reason, she enjoyed coming to see me on a regular basis, frequently requesting appointments as often as three times a week.

When Caron entered my life, I was going through some difficult personal times. Being in New York while my mother and brother struggled to make ends meet in Los Angeles kept me up many a night. And that's where I found a connection with Caron. I firmly believe that everyone—at every socioeconomic level and background, every race, color, or creed—*struggles*. It's a part of life for all of us.

Our family was struggling to keep our financial heads above water after my father passed away years before. He had been our guiding light, a man who had done absolutely *everything* for his family. When I was 16, he would drive my car to the gas station whenever he saw my tank was low. When my mother found a new job, he followed her to work making sure she didn't lose her way. And then we lost him.

Although I never got personal with Caron, I understood that she had lost something in her life—somewhere along the line—and turned to heroin for solace. She told me she was once a model. If so, she had become a shadow of the person she once had been. Her oral condition was atrocious. Her mouth spoke loudly of broken down, decayed, and missing teeth. She admitted to me that while addicted to heroin for ten years, hygiene of any kind was not high on her priority list. The only dental work she had received in the past was extractions. In her more coherent moments, Caron explained that she was seeing me because she was at a turning point in her life. She was going to clean up her act, start again with a clean slate, and make her life better. Given my personal circumstances, I understood full well that putting your life together after tragedy turns it upside down requires a helping hand. I found my own solace by putting in more time at school, studying harder, and working extra hours in the clinic.

While Caron never missed an appointment, I wish I could say I restored all her teeth and that she looked like a model again. But not all endings are perfect. The treatment she needed was so extensive I had only completed about half the required work by the time I left. When I graduated, she was transferred to a new fourth-year dental student.

In our last appointment, I asked Caron why she was so diligent and eager to come to the dental clinic when the majority of the patients I saw dreaded coming unless they were in aching pain. She looked at me with the forlorn expression of a five-year-old kid who had not received the love and attention she desired and needed—the love and attention every child deserves but doesn't always get. Softly she whispered, "'Cuz in my whole life, Dr. Park, ain't nobody ever treat me kind as you."

Jim Park, DDS

Reprinted by permission of Randy Glasbergen.

5

FOREIGN
INTRIGUE

It has eyes to see misery and want. It has ears to hear the sighs and sorrows of fellow men. That is what love looks like.

St. Augustine

Himalayan Quest

Life is something like this trumpet. If you don't put anything into it, you don't get anything out.

Jazzman William Handy

"Tashi delai, Tashi delai, Tashi delai," shouted the villagers who ran toward us from every direction. (It means, "Hello," in the language of Tibet.) *"Tashi delai, Tashi delai,"* they each chanted—mothers carrying babies, farmers with hoes, monks wearing long maroon robes, and laughing children with beautiful brown eyes.

The three village leaders came out of their huts to greet us. Word had arrived long before we did that a foreigner and two Tibetans from another village were coming to help those in pain. In this location, horns as long as twelve feet had been blown to call people from miles around.

We set up our makeshift clinic without delay using wooden planks for an operating table and big pots of boiling water to sterilize surgical instruments. Invariably, while long lines of patients quickly formed, we were offered the hospitality of salty Tibetan tea that tastes like seawater boiled with milk. Often in one day, between sunrise and dusk, we provided care for more than a hundred patients.

Head and neck infections—often the cause of excruciating pain—were the most common ailments. To this day, I find it hard to understand how these people can live as long as they do with such pain. For many, what had begun several years earlier as a simple dental cavity or minor gum infection subsequently spread through the face or neck causing massive infection.

With no electricity available, all surgery was done outdoors in the sunlight. A curious audience of water buffalo, goats, and people inevitably formed to observe the proceedings. In many cases, we began with the extraction of diseased teeth. The villagers then stared in amazement and disbelief as we went on to surgically remove cysts and, in some cases, tumors and then grafted new tissue over the resulting spaces. Those who watched gained courage since virtually no one complained of pain. When I finished each procedure, Sonam, my Tibetan assistant, would ask the patient, "Did you feel anything?"

Time after time, the crowds were amazed to hear the response: "No, nothing at all."

I was fascinated to discover that the villagers required only half as much local anesthetic as my patients back home in America. Since we were working high in the Himalayas where neither pharmacies nor mail service exists, I was thankful for their comparatively small need for pain medication; it effectively doubled our supply. This became particularly crucial after the general anesthetics we brought were lost in a terrifying accident on a mountain trail.

Considering our remote location, we felt fortunate to have so many types of therapies available. In the Himalayas, Western medicines—especially antibiotics along with surgery—are most highly regarded. But self-sufficiency in their medical care is certainly one of the greatest gifts they could acquire. For this reason, whenever possible, I preferred to focus on simple cures and procedures that could be used long after we were gone. For example, such elementary methods as washing with soap and boiled water to prevent infections, and adoption of a more balanced diet to prevent nutritionally related diseases such as blindness, should prove extremely helpful to them in the future.

My interpreter, a porter, and I walked from village to village carrying medications and instruments on our backs. Fording streams and rivers and hiking mountain trails near the Chinese border, we were dwarfed by the magnificent snow-capped peaks towering above us. These vistas, combined with breathtaking views of rushing white water and endless rice fields terraced on the mountainsides, provide some of the most exciting sights on earth. But it's the warmth of the people that gave me the greatest joy. While their health is poor and they have no money or modern technology, their smiles stretch from ear to ear. Everywhere we went villagers ran to greet us with their welcoming chant, eyes that sparkled with delight, and the inevitable salty Tibetan tea. I've worked in Appalachia and in some of America's most depressed urban slums, but I've never seen so many unhealthy people as I did in the Himalayas where even leprosy and tuberculosis are not uncommon.

It's quite clear that curative medicine (treating those who are already sick) will never provide the complete answer to the health problems we observed. The primary challenge is to institute changes to customs that have existed for thousands of years. So it was that wherever we went, we did our best to train the villagers in preventive medical and dental care and nutrition in the hope that they would adopt the practices for themselves and pass the information on to their children.

After returning home, I reflected on my reasons for going to the Himalayas and how much I had gained from the experience. Since life has always been good to me, there came a time in my career when I felt a strong need to help impoverished people who had no other way of receiving the aid my specialized training and experience offered. It was then that I journeyed to the other side of the world. Several years later, as I counted my blessings, I came to realize that the Tibetan belief in the laws of Karma, "As ye sow, so shall ye reap," had really come true for me.

Ira M. Klemons, DDS, PhD

The Four Amigas

I'll never forget my trips into the remote, interior mountain villages of Mexico. The only way to reach these places is by private airplane, landing on dirt runways hacked out of the primitive landscape. Except for a devoted group of medical and dental professionals, the inhabitants of these areas have no contact with modern healthcare. My fellow professionals and I paid our own expenses for air transportation, lodging, meals, bottled water, supplies, and equipment and took weekend "vacation" trips to care for the desperate health needs of this isolated population. These trips are usually arranged once a month, although most volunteers serve on rotation and participate only once or twice a year.

There are two groups I am aware of that make regular trips from California to Mexico—The Flying Doctors of Mercy (LIGA) and The Flying Samaritans. Most planes are four-passenger, single engine craft, so you can forget the lavatories, movies, and in-flight meal service. Instead, we flew—or bumped—along, "brown bagging" it while enjoying spectacular mountain and ocean views. As a registered dental hygienist—and as one who had recently received her private pilot, single engine land pilot's license—I was excited about this opportuty to combine my love of flying and adventure with my love for people and caring for their dental health needs.

I couldn't contain my excitement as we made our final approach on this, my first healthcare mission. As we landed, I looked out the windows and saw the smiling faces of several children who waved a warm welcome. Within minutes, the plane was followed by four other craft in our small fleet, and we soon had 16 assorted health care professionals—including nurses, opticians, surgeons, dentists, pharmacists, and one over-whelmed dental hygienist—standing on the dirt runway. A few minutes later, we climbed aboard a dilapidated old flatbed truck that transported us and our supplies to our final destination.

There were no paved streets in the village, only dirt roads. There was no electricity or running water. Of course, there were no sanitation facilities either. To serve our patients, we used flashlights, well water dispensed from buckets, and—as a spittoon—a cardboard box.

When we arrived at the little *clinica*, there were already more than 50 patients—in various stages of discomfort and pain—lined up for our services. Dressed in their Sunday best, they waited without complaint in the horribly hot sun. Many had walked for days through the mountains to reach our makeshift facility. My designated "assistants" were three girls, aged 9, 10, and 12. As I organized my instruments, cold sterile containers, and supplies in the best manner I could, I found myself in a crisis of self-confidence. *What am I doing here? I can't help these people. There's no water; there's no dental chair, there's no light. I can do so little, and they need so much!*

Then my long hours of professional training and my desire to help others pushed those thoughts from my head. I reminded myself, *You're the best they've got right now and they need your help. Stop whining and get to work!* I did, and I did.

My "assistants" helped by translating, holding the flashlight so I could see, and presenting the cardboard box for expectorated blood and saliva. They worked incredibly hard and were irresistibly sweet. They made me feel ashamed of my initial hesitation and doubts.

And so it went. I smiled, spoke my "dental Spanish," and gave every patient the very best care I could, sending each one home with a new toothbrush, tube of toothpaste, dental floss samples, and illustrated literature in Spanish. I showed each patient how to brush and rinse with salt water to speed healing in inflamed areas. They were thrilled when ugly stains were removed and they could see a clean smile in the mirror when we were done. For most, it was their first-time-ever dental cleaning. I concentrated my efforts on children and teens, as they had the best chance of preventing future problems if they would start improving their homecare right away.

When we finished work and began packing our equipment, I suddenly realized I was utterly fatigued and sore in places that had never been sore before. I gave my three assistants all the unused supplies, food, bottled water, and whatever else I thought might be of value for them. As I waved *adios* and started walking in the hot sun toward the landing strip, I heard them call my name. I turned as they came running up to me waving a broken umbrella. With smiles all around, they proudly opened the makeshift parasol and held it so as to protect my head from the rays of the sun. I bent over and hugged each child, holding back tears of joy. Then, *The Four Amigas* (my three new friends and I) walked hand-in-hand to the airplane where we exchanged one last round of hugs.

As the plane rolled down the runway and I waved my final farewells, I couldn't hold back the tears. What a glorious, professional, and personally fulfilling day! That is what all those years of schooling and training were for.

Shari Jay, RDH

A Picture in the Window

*It is astonishing how little one feels poverty when
one is loved.*

John Butler

The trip to the Dominican Republic was to be a working
vacation, but one to which I was looking forward. My life as
a private practice orthodontist involved a whirlwind of activity
every day in the office. Six dental chairs in an open operatory
and an extended duty dental assistant at each chair set the tone
for a busy schedule. Patient care, phone calls from mothers to
answer, and part time teaching in the orthodontic department
of our state dental college all combined to make me sometimes dream of Paradise—sandy tropical beaches and swaying
palm trees.

The invitation to "Paradise" came from one of my medical
colleagues. A group of physicians who had done short-term
(one- to three-week) medical missionary work outside of the
United States were presenting an evening seminar on their own
experiences. I attended the program.

Sure enough, while every slide had been photographed in

beautiful color and featured the professional activities of the medical group members, the "subliminal message" in each frame could not be missed—a background of beaches or palm trees. The speakers explained to the audience that while most of the medical specialties were represented on these trips, there were rarely any dentists, and the dental needs of the people were great. That night, I promised the group I would be on their next trip.

Two months later, as I sat in the Pan Am jet looking at the beautiful Caribbean beneath my window, I asked myself if I could really extract teeth after having practiced orthodontics exclusively since my residency at the University of Indiana. But I remembered my excellent oral surgery training while a student at Baylor Dental College. I knew that despite the years I still felt a sense of confidence and ease about the job to be done that, as I understood it, would be primarily extractions to relieve pain.

There was a routine to each day—awakening at 5:30, breakfast at 6:15, and off to work at 7:00. The patients stood in long lines of fifty yards or more waiting their turn to have painful, broken-down teeth extracted. The adults often earned less than $3 to $4 per day, and there was never excess money, even for the extraction of painful teeth. Although the surgical conditions were primitive, basic procedures were successfully performed on patient after patient with the result that much pain was relieved.

On my last working day, the missionary put me in his pickup truck and off we went for another routine day of "shucking teeth." As we drove along, I noticed that the road was getting worse and worse. I was about to ask where we were going when we stopped and the missionary announced, "Welcome to the Dominican Leper Hospital." A shudder ran through me as I recalled—in a flash—the stories I had read in the Bible about lepers. I had this alarming vision of going home with open sores on my body and being blind (a common affliction with lepers) when I returned to my family.

A Dominican order of nuns, primarily from Spain, spent a good part of their lives living with and caring for the lepers in this colony. A short, stocky Dominican nun explained in halting English that developing leprosy involved years of close contact with lepers and that I had nothing to fear. Somewhat relieved, I began to unpack my surgical instruments and supplies. Again, the work began and I was lost in my procedures for the time being.

I was practicing that day in a tin roof shed with a concrete (usually it was dirt) floor and a few windows with no glass in them. It had been a long, hot, tiring day, and I was not unhappy to hear that my last leprous patient was on the way. In a minute or two, a young Dominican nun came in the door helping an older man enter. He had one arm over her shoulder and his other arm rested on a crutch. It was an amazing sight!

While all my previous leper patients had been dressed in very worn clothing, this 80-plus-year-old gentleman had on what must have been his finest suit—white cotton—and a shirt adorned with a colorful tropical tie. His ensemble was topped off with a Panama straw hat. Leprosy had not been kind to him. He was blind, had lost all the fingers of one hand, and had only two fingers on the other. He had lost his left leg at the knee, and his bare right foot rested in a loose-fitting shoe.

When he was introduced to me, he dropped his crutch and—holding on to the nun—took off his hat. Bowing deeply, he said in excellent English, "Welcome to our village, *Señor* Doctor. Your kindness blesses us." I stood there transfixed by the courtly manner of this man who might just as easily have been the mayor presenting me with the key to his city. Recovering, I thanked him for coming, soon extracted four badly infected teeth, and bade my visitors goodbye.

As I stood by the window next to the table where I had

worked, I gazed out on the wondrous scene. There was the young nun helping the last patient up a gentle slope on the path back to his room. The two were chatting animatedly. As they turned their heads back and forth in conversation, I could see large smiles (the leper's was toothless) on both their faces. It was as if they had discovered something wonderful and couldn't talk enough about it.

Just at that instant, an isolated ray of sun broke through the cloud cover and shone exactly like a golden spotlight on the two of them. It was then—looking at a picture in the window of this hut in a leper colony—that I saw the story of what life was really about. The love of one person for another—the true sharing of one's life with another. Tears rolled down my cheeks as I realized I had been given a great gift...one I would cherish forever.

Charles W. Kenney, DDS

Volun-Tears

We must be the change we wish to see in the world.

Mahatma Gandhi

Some of the most exhilarating and enjoyable experiences I've had in the practice of dentistry were the seventeen years spent doing volunteer work in underdeveloped countries throughout the world. Almost every year I would take off four to six weeks and travel with my wife to places in the Caribbean, Africa, Central America, the Negev desert, the Philippines, and Hong Kong. Not only did we treat the underprivileged of these areas, but—in some cases—we also treated refugees from war-torn countries like Laos, Cambodia, and Vietnam.

Admittedly, the conditions we worked under were often unpleasant. The filth, the stench, the disease, and the poverty are difficult to imagine—or to tolerate for any length of time. Sometimes we worked many hours without rest under the most primitive conditions in jungle heat or Monsoon humidity. There were times when my "operatory" was furnished with nothing but an empty coffee can for a spittoon, a folding chair, and a flashlight. Nevertheless, my wife and I have always felt it was well worth it when one weighs all that against the satisfaction we got in meeting those challenges. We now enjoy fantastic memories not only of grateful patients but also of having the opportunity to see and live in some of the most beautiful and exotic places in the world.

Over the years, there have been many experiences I recall with fondness—and sometimes with tears. There was the time when the inmates at a state prison farm in Belize made me a souvenir model ship because, as they said, "Dr. Kutler, we have never been treated so good." Another time, my wife and I were honored with a personal "thank you" excursion to Jerusalem as guests of the Prime Minister of Israel. But of all the nice things that we have experienced, there is still one that seems to stay with us forever. It happened on our fourth trip to Haiti.

The lady who established and ran the *Fondation Pedodontique d'Haiti* was a woman who had been trained at the Columbia University Dental School and had come back to do what she could to help the poor of her native land. Using her clinic in Port-au-Prince as a base, we traveled to the surrounding areas each day to provide care for a tragically impoverished population. Shortly after we arrived, our host showed us pictures of one of her patients, a young girl of about eight or nine. The first photograph revealed that the right side of the child's face was normal—and really quite beautiful. But the photo also showed a benign tumor on the left side that had caused her face to swell to two or three times its normal size. The riveting image was as pitiful as it was grotesque.

Madam Leroy, pronounced *Lu wah'*, told us that arrangements had been made for the tumor to be removed gratis at the University of Florida, but that there were no funds available for the child's transportation. She asked if we would be willing to help. Without hesitation—without even looking at each other for confirmation—my wife and I agreed to pay for all travel costs. At that point, we both were startled to see Madam Leroy fall to her knees, put her arms around our legs, and literally shout to the heavens, "Praise the Lord! Praise the Lord!" Even though it was embarrassing for us, the moment was certainly touching and dramatic. But it didn't begin to prepare us for what was to happen the next day.

The following afternoon, Madam Leroy took me away from a patient and asked me to step outside. Standing in the shade was a Haitian lady with a young girl. On seeing me, the mother gave her daughter a slight nudge and the child came forward. Unlike some of the youngsters we had seen around the grounds, this petite little girl was spotless; and her long red dress, although slightly tattered as a hand-me-down might be, was clean. Her hair had been carefully braided for this meeting. Even though she was shy, she started speaking to me with a sweet soft voice in a language I didn't understand—a patois combining Creole and French. Nevertheless, there was a part of me that very clearly understood what she was saying, "Thank you for helping me look pretty again." I knelt down and she put her thin little arms around my neck. As we hugged, my heart just melted away. Even now as I write this and remember that moment, my heart swells and my throat tightens—I can't hold back the tears.

As professionals in the health field, the primary mission of all dentists is to help people. As a volunteer, that purpose is magnified enormously. And while the perception might be that we are being altruistic and magnanimous, any medical mission veteran will tell you the reality is that the volunteer is the one who benefits most. All of those whom we have touched, and especially that little Haitian girl, will always live in my heart and enrich my life forever.

Sol Kutler, DDS

From Russia with Love

This is the hour to do good.

Words displayed on a large clock
in a downtown city of Argentina

I first met Dmitri when he came into my office with his brother, Mikhail. Mikhail had recently moved to our town to work as a scientist at the nearby Los Alamos Laboratory. Mikhail spoke English and translated for Dmitri who spoke only Russian.

"Dmitri has tooth hurting, and I know he has lots problems in his mouth but not much money. I have dental insurance, but it only covers my wife and me. I have five hundred dollars I can use for Dmitri's teeth to be fixed or maybe a little more if something looks important to be fixed. He was in terrible mine accident in Ural Mountains and spent three years in hospital before he came to stay with us awhile. He is mining engineer but will never be able to go back to mines." With this introduction, Mikhail left my office to return to work leaving his brother behind while I began a thorough oral examination of my new Russian patient.

Since the breakup of the old Soviet Union, numerous scientists from Eastern Europe have migrated to the West and the Los Alamos Laboratory has hired a number of these immigrants. I have treated several of these wonderful people in my practice and have consistently been distressed by the poor quality of the dental care they received in Russia. Problems include numerous partially filled root canals, poorly fitting stainless steel crowns, crumbling fillings, and widespread gum disease.

I noticed from the health history that Dmitri was forty-three and in generally good health. His physical appearance was thin and perhaps a little frail—undoubtedly from the long hospital stay following his mining accident. His left sleeve was empty except for a prosthetic "hook" that he held as inconspicuously as possible. His countenance was what could be described as downcast or discouraged and, as is common with Eastern Europeans, he was an obvious smoker. Despite all this, there was that unmistakable inner strength that I have observed in all of my Russian patients.

Oral examination revealed old stained and crumbling fillings, a "one size fits nobody" stainless steel bridge, a few areas of decay, and widespread gum inflammation. With my limited Russian and Dmitri's equally limited English, we were able to establish the "zube" (tooth) that was hurting. Clearly his brother's offer of five hundred dollars wouldn't go very far in restoring Dmitri's mouth to Western standards. With the miracle of local anesthetic, we repaired Dmitri's decayed molar and then set up his next appointment.

For the second appointment and several subsequent visits, Dmitri was unaccompanied. The dental care proceeded slowly as we performed root planing, a root canal, crown, and numerous other restorations. To make new appointments, we would point to days on a calendar and iterate in Russian a number to indicate the time of appointment. Occasionally, we would send notes home with Dmitri for his brother to translate regarding post-op instructions, etc. Beyond these efforts, there was no communication between us, yet I began to feel a growing closeness to Dmitri. God led me to the conclusion that I could not charge him or his brother for the work I was doing. In fact at one appointment I felt led to give Dmitri a small gift, a Russian Bible for which he struggled to say thank you. I was reminded of a statement by Ravi Zacharias, the evangelist, who said you don't need to go abroad to minister to other nations because there are so many people from other parts of the world here in the United States. My work with Dmitri enabled me to experience perhaps a little of the thrill that missionary doctors feel when they know their work is to glorify God.

As the appointments came and went, I did my very best to serve Dmitri's dental needs. Then one day in October, I pointed to a date on the calendar to schedule his next visit. Dmitri shook his head and said, "*Moscva*," to indicate he was returning home. I selected an earlier day and time and he nodded assent. The appointment time agreed upon was a Monday morning at 11:30, a timeslot I usually reserved for emergencies; but I wanted one last opportunity to do what I could for Dmitri.

At our final appointment, Mikhail was with Dmitri when I entered the operatory. He said Dmitri was leaving for Russia; and he wondered if there was anything I wanted to tell him before he left. I thought for a minute and said, "There will be no charge for any of the dental services for Dmitri."

Mikhail looked shocked, answered that this was "too much to be accepted," and said that they must pay for the work. I told him I was touched by their care for one another, felt it a privilege to be able to help Dmitri, and thought that perhaps I would try to visit him in Russia someday. Mikhail left to go back to work after quickly exchanging a few words in Russian with his brother.

When we seated Dmitri for this last appointment, I was already running late. I realized that if I was to finish in time for the staff to have a lunch break, I would need to scale back my plans for an overly ambitious treatment session. As I started replacing some of the discolored and failing fillings in Dmitri's front teeth, I couldn't bear the thought of leaving any of the unsightly restorations. Instead, I opted to remove all of the old fillings in his front teeth and just leave time problems to the Inventor of time. I worked with the realization that I was working for God.

Refusing to look at the clock, we pursued the fillings with newly found energy and finished restyling Dmitri's smile with more esthetic restorations. Just as I finished polishing the last of the fillings and set the chair up, the church chime across the street from my office intoned twelve o'clock and I was reminded I was working on God's time.

As he turned to leave, Dmitri uttered the longest sentence I ever heard him speak in English: "You here four?" I confirmed that I would be in the office until six. At four o'clock, the receptionist came to the operatory where I was working and announced that Dmitri was there with Mikhail and wanted to talk to me. I thought perhaps he had some questions about the work or wanted to thank me.

Mikhail was the eloquent spokesman. "Dmitri wants thank you for gift of dental care."

I looked at Dmitri and immediately saw a change. He was positively glowing. His face bore a big smile and a look of excited expectation. Mikhail continued, "In Ural Mountains, they mine the most beautiful jasper in the world. It has been used to great advantage in Louvre in Paris and in Hermitage in St. Petersburg. Dmitri has made this with his one hand from jasper and would give it for you."

At this point, Dmitri held out a beautiful box of delicate

design polished to a high luster. The container was about seven inches long by three inches square and made with perfect seams. The jasper was a stunning combination of green-gray and chestnut brown.

I looked at the two brothers and said, "There was to be no payment for the dental work."

Mikhail answered, "Oh, this is not *payment*. This is *gift!*"

I said, "It is beautiful, and I am humbled by your gift. Thank you."

As the brothers left the office, Mikhail added, "And Dmitri wants you visit him in Russia."

J. D. Matthews, DDS, MS

Caribbean Gold

A mouth without molars is like a mill without a stone;
and a tooth is more precious than a diamond.

Don Quixote in *Man of La Mancha* by Miguel de Cervantes

Soon after graduating from dental school, I found myself jetting off to the Caribbean islands of Trinidad and Tobago in the West Indies. My destination, Piarco International Airport in Port-of-Spain, Trinidad, certainly sounds like the gateway to a romantic adventure. Was I taking an exotic vacation to unwind following a long and trying professional education? No, indeed. I had volunteered my dentistry skills to SERVOL—a grassroots organization dedicated to helping the youth of this tiny twin-island republic.

As I stepped off the plane, I immediately wilted in the ninety-degree heat and ninety three percent humidity. I had been warned, though, that this weather was normal in a locale just eleven degrees north of the Equator.

Why was I there? I had asked myself that question repeatedly on the flight in. Right out of school, I could have launched a satisfying career in my father's practice. Dad's office was in a great location and served a large patient pool in an upwardly mobile community. I could have made a dandy living right from the start. Instead, I'd decided to set up shop in a shanty-town 5,000 miles from home. Why did I do it? Read on and I'll tell you.

For the next two years, I barely made enough money to cover interest on my educational loans. The clinic's fee schedule was separated into two categories. Local, school-aged children were charged just a few Trinidad dollars, the equivalent of spare change in U.S. currency, for almost all procedures. (The directors of the program felt there should be a nominal charge so as to create a sense of worth for what patients received.)

Mind you, a "few Trinidad dollars" was not an easy thing for these island kids to come by. The clinic's income was supplemented by "outside" patients—anyone else needing dental care. This group paid full fees. That way, the clinic stayed out of the red...most of the time.

For the first year, I delivered primary care dentistry consisting mainly of extractions and very large fillings. One day, a boy of 15 sat in my chair complaining of pain in one of his teeth. After my initial look into his mouth, I stood back and asked, "Which one?" Almost every tooth was decayed beyond repair. After a few silver fillings and many extractions, it was time to address his upper front teeth.

Due to the rather large, black, semi-circular decayed areas on both sides of each incisor, Davis' self esteem was almost non-existent. This problem had haunted him since the age of six when his then-white pearls first made their way through the gum tissue. The new teeth were quite unprepared for the onslaught of a diet incredibly high in refined sugar, a product of the island's primary crop, sugar cane. (Hygiene education and diet management didn't exist in Trinidad at the time.) The boy was so self-conscious about his unsightly teeth he always held a hand over his mouth while talking or laughing.

Davis' situation was a special one. All four upper incisors needed either root canal treatment or extraction due to the extent of the decay. Having lost most of his molars, he had already become what some would describe as a "dental cripple." There was no way I was going to remove the last hope this kid had to be able to speak, laugh, eat, and function as a vital person.

Davis and I made a pact. My job was the easy one. I removed the extensive decay, performed root canal therapy, and then needed to place permanent restorations. Three of the teeth, though challenging, were restored with tooth-colored composite resin fillings. Then came the real problem. The one remaining central incisor had become so decayed that the only recourse was to place a crown on it.

Up to this point, Davis had kept his end of the bargain. He completed payment for the work already done at a total cost of about ten U.S. dollars. He also started to take care of his mouth in a way I hadn't seen with any of the other kids. The boy seemed to actually care about what was happening to his oral health. His gum tissues no longer bled, and his plaque level dropped to nothing. But now we faced the possibility of having to extract the remaining incisor. A crown fee was certainly well beyond his financial capability. So, with the approval of the program director, I proposed to provide a crown at a cost equal to the laboratory fabrication charges.

Even at this reduced fee, 127 Trinidad dollars seemed like a million to Davis. I told him that we would proceed with placing the crown when he came up with the money. Through the local shantytown grapevine, I was told of Davis' exploits to earn money for his crown. With employment very hard to come by in Trinidad, this youngster took it upon himself to create jobs where none had existed before. He performed every odd job imaginable, from collecting empty beer bottles for deposit refunds to helping people carry groceries to their cars at the local store. Over time, the money started to accumulate—quite literally—penny by penny.

After two months, Davis returned to the clinic grinning ear-to-ear as he slapped down a stack of 127 red-colored Trinidad dollar bills. He asked if he could get the crown that day and was disappointed when I told him we needed to prepare the tooth and take an impression of it for the lab. I explained that the whole process would take approximately three weeks. Due to a timely "no show" by another patient, we were able to start on preparations for the crown right away.

Davis jumped into the chair, eagerly awaiting the whine of the drill. I finished the procedure by taking a color match so that the porcelain crown would blend with the fillings in his other incisors. Davis appeared agitated as I dismissed him from the appointment with a temporary crown in place. As he peered into the mirror to look at my handiwork, he asked if the permanent crown would have to look just like the temporary. Frankly, I thought my temporary crown matched his teeth quite nicely. Without a thought, I quickly assured him that the lab technician was a wizard at making porcelain crowns—better than some I had seen back in the States. Davis still seemed perplexed. He then said, "Doc, why I can't get a *gold* crown?"

A gold crown he got!

Now, many years later, I'm back in the U.S. where each day passes without ceremony. The commuter traffic seems to get worse and worse. The list of government rules regulating our profession grows relentlessly. Like other dentists, I make endless entries into patient charts during and after each appointment to protect myself in case of medical-legal issues. I trudge through yet another electronic voice mail system trying desperately to speak to a real person regarding insurance coverage for my patients. Beads of sweat still roll over my cheeks, though these days I feel it's due more to stress than the presence of high humidity. But whenever I feel I'm slipping below the surface...feeling like that next breath just may not come...all I have to do is think back to a young boy and be reminded of why I became a dentist.

In the final months before I left that wonderful little island, I saw the flash of a truly brilliant smile from time to time...and the face of a boy deservedly proud of what he had worked so hard to get. It is now thirteen years later, and I am absolutely positive his smile of Caribbean gold *still* glitters brightly.

Laurence M. Brownstein, DDS

Leonardo

The soul is healed by being with children.

Fyodor Dostoyevski

My wife Sylvia has a heart of gold. During our engagement, she took several weeks off to participate in a church mission to war ravaged Honduras. When she returned, she told me how the things she saw there had changed her life. In that tropical waste-land, with the sounds of machine gun fire in the distance, she saw hoards of Nicaraguan refugees cross into Honduras. Among them were starving children—many orphaned or aban-doned. In one case, she told me about a child whose only "food" the previous day was a discarded banana peel.

When Sylvia first told me about her trip, the events she described seemed more like a TV documentary than true life. Nevertheless, her stories touched my heart and her example was a real inspiration. Not long after Sylvia's return from Nicaragua, I graduated from dental school and we were mar-ried. When we got back from our honeymoon, Sylvia volun-teered our services for a trip to Nicaragua with the Baptist Medical and Dental Missions.

Before long, we found ourselves in a van lumbering down a muddy road to a village 30 miles south of Managua. It was surreal—I felt like we had gone back in time a hundred years. For most, travel was on foot or, for the very fortunate, ox drawn cart. These friendly, dark skinned people had never seen a doctor or dentist in their lifetime.

I quickly buckled down to the tasks at hand. Lines to the clinic formed three hours before we awoke at sunrise. By ten in the morning, the ninety nine-degree-heat had already sapped my strength. One after another, I extracted decayed teeth that had been tormenting their owners for years. Working at a pace of nearly one hundred and fifty teeth a day, I barely noticed the dirty, cherubic faced seven-year-old tugging at the seat of my green scrub pants. "Where ees Seelvia?" he asked in the best English he could muster. When I looked at him, all I could see were eyes—huge eyes magnified behind ridiculously large, round, ladies glasses. "Where ees Seelvia?" he implored. When I finally found out what had so thoroughly bound this curious child, Leonardo, to my wife, it changed my heart forever.

During the first two days of the trip, Sylvia had spent part of her time sterilizing dental instruments. Unbeknownst to me, the medical director had also asked her to handle the sorting and distribution of eyeglasses—old discarded glasses donated in the U.S. Besides having a warm heart, Sylvia is a brilliant manager and soon had an assembly line operation underway. Rows of glasses from weak to very strong with bifocals were tried out by looking at the small text in a Bible and an eye chart.

One of the "customers" my wife spotted was a cute seven-year-old busily trying on one pair of spectacles after another. Sylvia greeted Leonardo and worked through the rows with him until they got to the strongest optics, usually reserved for the very aged and infirm. The boy put the large bifocals on and looked at the grass, the sky, and finally his mothers face. Tears filled the oversized lenses as it became obvious to everyone the boy was seeing his mother's face for the first time in his young life.

For the rest of the trip, Leonardo was a permanent fixture at my wife's side. When he lost sight of her, he simply walked into the clinic and pulled at the rear end of my scrubs until I stopped to pay attention to him, excused myself from patient and assistant, and directed him to where I thought she was.

Sylvia and I grew very close to Leonardo and seriously considered adopting him. After meeting with his family and the authorities, though, the consensus was that Leonardo would be more valuable to his extended family as a breadwinner than he would be as our heart warmer. Reluctantly, we left Leonardo and Nicaragua, leaving behind our love and, especially, our hearts. But through this adventure I returned home with an entirely new and improved one.

Robert S. Quintano, DDS

6

KIDS AT THE DENTAL OFFICE

On losing his first tooth: "Mom, Mom, look! Now I have a window in my smile!"

Paul Clark, six years old,
as told by his mother, Rachel Clark
Heidelberg, Germany

Don't Lie to Grandma

Late summer. Midnight. Saturday. I was sound asleep when the telephone rang. Since I was the doctor on call for my dental practice that weekend, the phone rang both in my home and at my answering service. After two rings, the service picked up the line and the phone stopped disturbing my sleep.

A few minutes later, the phone rang again—this time more insistently. "This is your service. We've just received a call from a very concerned woman about her grandson, Todd, who has a terribly painful toothache." The service then gave me the grandmother's number.

I thanked the service operator and then placed a call to the concerned grandmother. When Mrs. Thomas answered, I could hear a child in obvious distress crying loudly in the background. "This is Dr. Patterson. May I help you?"

"Yes, thank you for calling back so quickly. I've called several dentists around town located closer to me, but you're the only one to answer back. My grandson, Todd, has been crying all night with an awful toothache. His mother, a single mom, lives in Indiana with his sisters and younger brother. To give her a rest, I've been taking care of the boy for the summer.

He'll be going home again to start school in just a few weeks—right after Labor Day."

I then asked the usual dental questions: "How long has the tooth been hurting? How old is Todd? [He was seven.] Which side of his face is hurting—top or bottom? What have you done for him so far?" After gaining some insights on the little guy, I concluded I had to see him that very night. By then, it was 12:30 in the morning.

I met Grandma and Todd at the office 30 minutes later. The boy was really crying by then and I could tell he was in great pain. No sooner had I started my examination than I realized I'd need help with this little fellow. Even though the hour was late, I called my faithful dental assistant, Ethel—a grandmother herself—who lived just a few minutes from my office. Obviously Ethel was sleeping when I called, but she answered the phone on the second ring and said she'd be right over.

Todd's tooth was badly abscessed and his face was swollen. I told his grandmother we'd have to remove that nasty tooth right away. She agreed, and my assistant and I proceeded to do just that. Todd did his best to cooperate, and by 1:30, the abscessed tooth was successfully extracted. Soon after, the patient appeared to be 100% better. After thanking Ethel and me with great big hugs, Todd visited the "treasure box" to select a toy—his reward for being such a good patient. We all then headed home for more badly needed sleep.

Later that morning, I arose at my usual 6:00 AM to read the Good Book and prepare for church. Several hours later, during the service, my pager silently alerted me. I excused myself and made a call from the church office to my answering service. It was Grandma again. She told me Todd had slept very comfortably most of the night but was now again in pain with a swollen face. I arranged to meet the two at the office right away.

Now this was challenging. Todd had *another* abscessed

tooth he had not had a problem with before. It too needed extraction. And again, he was *sooooo* happy to have the pain gone after the procedure. Now, I thought to myself, this would be the last time I'd ever see this little chap. I was mistaken.

The following day, I was back at the office with all my staff where everything was running like the usual Monday—goodness-how-things-pile-up-on-the-weekend—morning. No sooner had Ethel and I finished telling the others about our adventures with Todd than my phone rang. You guessed it. Grandma.

"Todd has another toothache and is crying," my secretary announced.

"Tell her to bring him in right away," I said.

Todd and his grandmother soon arrived. I proceeded to examine the boy and asked Grandma where the pain was and how long he'd been complaining about it. She said the symptoms had started Sunday night and seemed to bother him off and on again since then with no real focus.

I repeated my examination—but much more thoroughly this time. I probed, pushed, and thumped. Try as I might, I couldn't find a tooth that should give pain. I said to Todd, "Do you *really* have a toothache?"

He dropped his little head and slowly confessed, "No, sir."

"You told your grandmother you had one last night. Did you lie to her, Todd?"

"Yes, I did doctor."

"Why did you fib to your grandmother like this, Todd?"

"Because I was lonely and scared and missed my mama, and I wanted Grandma to come and lie down by me."

"I think your Gran would have come lie down by you if you'd just asked her," I said. Then, in a loving tone of voice, I inquired, "Todd, is there anything *else* bothering you?"

"Well," he said slowly, "I was thinking...while we were driving to your office...." He paused and caught his sobbing voice.

"What were you thinking, Todd?" I asked, coaxing him to tell me his troubles.

"I...was...thinking...," he slowly drew out his words—and then just blurted out the rest, "that you would make a great DAD for me!"

My eyes just filled with tears—as did Grandma's eyes and my assistant's eyes. I pulled the boy to me and gave him a Dad-sized hug. Then I decided to share my own story with him.

"Todd, your grandmother has told me you're seven years old. When I was seven, I lost my mom and dad to cancer—both in the same year. I was sent to live in an orphanage with my two brothers."

Todd's eyes got really big. "But who took care of you?" he wanted to know.

"My grandmother," I said, "just like your grandmother who loves you. Even though I was in an orphanage a long way from my grandmother's house, she would take the train and come see my brothers and me every weekend. And she'd always write us letters. Now, Todd, no more fibs to Grandma. Let's have another big hug."

"Thank you, doctor. I love you."

"And I love you, too, Todd."

Todd left the office walking very tall with a smile on his little face. One week later we received a note from his grandmother: "Dr. Patterson, you don't know what this dental problem has done for Todd. It has changed his life. He is not lying anymore. He talks about you every day. And he is so thankful to your staff who showed so much love. Thank you again, Dr. Patterson, for caring and for loving Todd. He needed that very much!"

Norman A. Patterson, DDS

Masked Lady

As was my custom, I previewed the schedule of dental hygiene patients I'd be working with that special fall day. I noticed with some apprehension a late afternoon appointment that was one of those patients who could either be the highlight of my day or the most draining. Of course, I'm talking about a three-year-old coming in for his first dental visit. This particular little boy turned out to be adorable and, to my great relief, happily did everything I requested. Not only was I able to take "pictures" of his teeth, I also completed "brushing" his teeth with the "tickling polisher."

It was near the end of his procedure that the boy gave me, and everyone else in the office, the laugh of the day. I had just finished polishing his teeth and was about to offer him a cup of water with which to rinse out the toothpaste.

Before putting the cup to his lips, I explained that I wanted him to swish the water in his mouth and let "Mr. Thirsty Straw" take it out for him. I could tell by the questioning look on his face that the boy didn't understand what I meant by "swishing." To give him a visual, I lowered my dental mask and made the swishing motion with my own mouth. He was successfully able to rinse, swish, and suction the water out with Mr. Thirsty Straw.

Afterward, he looked me straight in the eye with the sweet, honest innocence of a young child and announced in an unexpectedly loud voice, "YOU KNOW, YOU LOOK A LOT BETTER WITH THE MASK ON!"

Not only did *I* burst into laughter, but so did every patient, all the assistants, our receptionist, and the dentists present in our very open-spaced office!

Josette Beach, RDH, MS

Colorblind

It was young Franklin's first dental visit—ever. After reviewing Frankie's medical form with his mother, I turned to the boy and asked, "You don't smoke, do you?"

"No way," he answered.

I then asked if he knew the reason not to smoke. While he was thinking of an appropriate answer, I explained, "Smoking makes your lungs turn black."

With the innocence of a five-year-old, and with brown eyes as big as saucers, Frankie replied, "What's wrong with that? Then they will match the rest of me."

That's when I realized I was truly colorblind.

Rosalyn Shraiar, RDH

Persuasive Dentistry

My first patient of the day was a cute little four-year-old. Her mom pulled me aside and explained that the child had been a thumb-sucker since birth. The woman said that she and her husband had tried everything they knew of to get the girl to stop. But nothing worked.

I reassured the mother and sat down with the daughter. I spoke with the child for several minutes and gave her all the good reasons to stop sucking her thumb.

The girl thought for a moment, looked up at her mother and me, and announced, "Okay, I'll never suck my thumb again!"

The mother's jaw dropped open in disbelief. I felt justifiably proud of myself—and my powers of persuasion.

As I started to walk out of the room, the girl looked up and asked, "Which finger can I suck?"

Brad Shwidock, DMD

Clean as a Hound's Tooth

It never fails to amaze me how children can look through you, size you up, and make judgments about you no matter what they have heard about dentistry from parents, their peers, or by way of street talk.

Several years ago, I had a cute little seven-year-old who came in for her first visit to the dentist. The hygienist cleaned her teeth, fluoridated them, and instructed this youngster on the importance of good homecare. When the hygiene procedures were completed, I entered the operatory and performed a routine examination of the child's mouth. I, too, stressed the importance of good homecare. The girl proceeded to tell me that not only did she brush her own teeth regularly, she also brushed her dog's teeth every single day.

I laughed and told her I hoped she didn't use *her* toothbrush to clean the dog's teeth. She looked at me, placed her hands on her hips, and said she would *never* use *her* toothbrush—she used her *sister's* brush instead. After laughing so hard that tears came to my eyes, I instructed the hygienist to give this little girl three toothbrushes; one for herself, one for her sister, and one for her dog. I am certain that good homecare now exists throughout that household.

Merritt Dean Halem, DDS

Garfield ® by Jim Davis

A Tingling Sensation

I'm beginning to lose my smile.

Anonymous five-year-old after successful anesthesia

It had only been a year since I graduated from dental school, but I'd already discovered the importance of phrasing questions to my patients in the right way. I found this to be especially critical when dealing with the very young—they will answer "Yes" to just about anything you ask.

One afternoon I was making preparations to fill a small cavity in five-year-old Johnny's lower right molar. Several minutes had passed since I had given him an injection of anesthetic. Instead of asking, "Are you numb?" I asked, "How does your lip feel?"

As he pondered my question, he sat there in the chair with his legs crossed and his blue eyes looking upward and to the left. He then gave me the most honest answer I have ever received: "It kind of feels like my legs do when my mother leaves me on the toilet too long."

Gary D. Sellers DDS

The Perfect Job

My hygiene patient that afternoon was Justin, a nine-year-old who had been coming in twice a year for routine checkups since the age of three. Due to proper homecare and regular visits to the dentist, he had always been cavity free and his only experience with our office involved preventative procedures. As a result, the bulk of Justin's appointment time had been spent in my care with the dentist only performing a brief exam—generally referred to as "counting teeth" to minimize childhood fears—at the conclusion of each visit. The boy, always cooperative and compliant, had never been very talkative—almost to the point of being shy. On this particular afternoon, though, Justin appeared to be deep in thought. When the visit was almost over, he inquired if he could ask me a few questions.

I told him I'd do my best to answer. Justin first asked what my job was called and then inquired as to exactly what it was that dental hygienists did. Next, he asked what the job performed by the man in the white coat in our office was called. He knew the man was called "Doctor" but he didn't know how the doctor's job was referred to. I told him the doctor was a dentist, and I asked him why he wanted to know. That's when Justin told me he wanted to grow up to be a dentist. When I asked why, the boy said, "Well, the dental hygienist does the cleaning, x-rays, fluoride treatments, and brushing and flossing instructions. Then the dentist comes in and counts my teeth. Since I can already count, being a dentist is the perfect job for me."

Jackie S. Perry, RDH

"Fancy jack you have here, Doc.
What will it be today,
oil change or front wheel alignment?"

The Secret

As a student in dental school, it often seemed to me that the main focus was on fulfilling requirements necessary for graduation. We had to complete a certain number of bridges, crowns, root canals, amalgams, composites, dentures, etc. to qualify. One of the requirements was to complete restorations on children in the pediatric clinic. For me, it was hard enough to satisfactorily complete a filling on a cooperative adult, let alone a squirmy child.

One particular afternoon, I had to complete a filling on a rather rambunctious six-year-old. I'd worked on him before and had achieved marginal success in gaining his cooperation. It goes without saying that I was probably more apprehensive than he was about this appointment.

I was surprised when I went to the waiting area to find a sedate, almost depressed, young man. As I sat him in the dental chair, I inquired as to why he was so sad. He informed me he had lost a footrace at school—to a GIRL! While I comforted him on his courageous attempt to race—and not on the fact that he had lost—I noticed he had his left shoe on his right foot and his right shoe on his left foot. Not to pass up an opportunity, I promised to tell him a "secret" at the end of our appointment on how he could run faster if we finished the filling without a lot of fuss. Anticipating some miraculous words of advice, he promised to cooperate.

We must have finished in record time. The boy was a perfect patient and I was delighted at what we were able to accomplish. Glowing in my performance, I temporarily forgot about the "secret." My patient, however, was not about to forget. Eyes full of hope, he reminded me of my promise to tell him how he could run faster.

I leaned over the boy with my mouth close to his right ear and, in hushed tones, told him the secret: *"You have your shoes on the wrong feet!"*

Within seconds, disappointment and sadness returned to his face. "What's wrong?" I asked.

In a dejected voice that I'll never forget, he answered, *"But these are the only feet I have!"*

Gary E. Heyamoto, DDS, FAGD

7

MEMORABLE PATIENTS

Resolve to be tender with the young, compassionate with the aged, sympathetic with the striving, tolerant with the weak, and forgiving with the wrong; for sometime in your life you will have been all of these.

Lloyd Shearer

What Are You in For?

To keep you teeth in good condition, see your dentist twice a year and mind your own business.

Ann Landers

It always amazes me when people of different life experience and happenstance make a meaningful connection. Such was the case several months ago when I had two inmates from the local county jail visit my office for dental care.

As a security precaution, prisoners are always escorted to the office in handcuffs and wearing manacles. That day, one wore a black and white horizontally striped uniform whereas the other was dressed in safety orange. Both men were pleasant enough to work on, but I still wondered about the perceptions of other patients when I worked on prisoners. After all, it's not always comfortable to sit in a dental office under normal conditions. Try sharing a waiting room with an armed policeman and two men in restraints!

My unfounded fears came to a screeching halt that afternoon when our 3:30 patient, Amanda, arrived. She had just gotten out of school and had walked to our office from the junior high a short distance away. Apparently undaunted by the threesome in the waiting room, she quickly struck up a conversation with the man in the bright orange uniform. Casting judgment aside, she asked him simply and fearlessly, "What are you in for?"

Without hesitation, the prisoner responded, "A filling."

John J. Johnson, DDS

Ten Years and Counting

*Preventive dentistry can
extend human life ten years.*

Charles Mayo, founder of the Mayo Clinic

Vella was one of our favorite patients. Married more than 70 years, she and her husband were both the same age. Like her husband, Vella was a ray of sunshine—still knowledgeable and interesting in spite of her advanced age. Our staff learned something new every time the couple visited our office.

At 96, Vella still had nearly all her natural teeth—although most of them were worn and broken. Nevertheless, she came in regularly to have them cleaned. The passing years had also taken their toll on Vella's good nature—she had grown more and more cantankerous.

During a recent cleaning, Vella must have asked me every five minutes "Who *are* you? And what are you doing to me?"

Each time, I answered, "Vella, I'm Adrienne, and I'm cleaning your teeth for you."

When I was nearly finished with the cleaning, she grabbed the armrests, raised herself bolt upright on her elbows, and demanded in a loud, cranky tone, "WHO *ARE* YOU? AND

WHAT ARE YOU DOING TO ME?"

Patiently, I explained, "Vella, I'm Adrienne, and I've been cleaning your teeth for the last ten years."

With considerable irritation, she hollered, "AND YOU'RE NOT DONE *YET*?"

Adrienne Gonzales, RDH

Of Teeth and Trust

*Character is the ability to say "No" when
everyone except your conscience is screaming
"Yes!"*

Richie Harris

It was the summer of 1956. I had graduated from dental
school the previous year and was the new dental officer aboard
a U.S. Navy troop transport carrying Army and Air Force personnel from the mainland to England and Germany. As the ship
steamed eastward in the English Channel, my Sunday afternoon
nap abruptly ended with the ringing of my room telephone. I
lifted the receiver to hear the Captain bark into my ear, "Doc,
I'll be in your office in ten minutes. I want you to yank out a
no-good broken tooth!" After phoning my corpsman, Don, to
set up the office, I hurried to get ready for "The Old Man."

Just as Don and I finished our preparations, the Captain
appeared in the doorway. He was a short, barrel-chested man
with a no-nonsense attitude, and he oozed exhaustion. He had
been up all night as the ship sailed through the English Channel
and into the North Sea. Although a Channel pilot had been on
board all this time, the Old Man just didn't trust some Limey to

guide "his ship" through these waters!

As the Captain sank wearily into the dental chair, he growled, "Get this darned tooth out and do it fast!" (He didn't really say, "darned," but you get the idea.) I inspected the troublesome molar as our ship's commander eyed me warily. A filling had fractured along with a small portion of the tooth. Extraction did not seem indicated. I explained this to the Captain and also told him I would need to take an x-ray before beginning treatment. "I don't want any darned x-ray, just get that bugger out of there!" he retorted.

My knees felt wobbly, and Don's eyes caught mine with a questioning look. "Captain, I really can't do anything without an x-ray."

"Doc, pull that darned tooth NOW," he snapped.

After a few seconds which certainly seemed much longer, I looked directly at the Captain and said, "Sir, I have never sailed on a ship this size, and I know nothing about its operation. But you are the ship's Captain, and I trust your judgment completely. You, Sir, know nothing about teeth, and you need to trust me as the ship's dental officer."

He turned and glared at me for several interminable seconds through tired, bloodshot eyes before thundering, "Doctor, take your blooming x-ray and be quick about it!"

Phew! The tension was broken. The x-ray revealed that there was no nerve involvement. "The tooth does not need to come out, Sir," I explained. "It requires a new filling which I can do for you now."

"Do it, then!" he ordered.

A blur of activity followed: anesthetic injection; whine of the dental drill; Don handing me instruments; retaining band placed around the tooth; amalgam mixed and packed into the newly prepared cavity; final carving of the filling; and removal of the band. I instructed the Captain to avoid chewing on the right side, and Don scheduled an appointment in two days for the final polishing and bite check. The Captain mumbled something unintelligible as he vacated the dental chair and exited the office. To celebrate the successful conclusion of the Captain's treatment, Don went down to the galley and brought back two steaming cups of coffee. We both heaved sighs of relief and took a well-deserved break as the ship continued on its way toward Germany.

Our ship carried not only troops but their dependents as well. Two Navy nurses took excellent care of the women and children on board in addition to staying in the Captain's good graces. Every few weeks, they prepared a delicious batch of fudge and invited the Captain to join the other officers in the Officers' Lounge for coffee and fudge. The Old Man truly enjoyed these parties. Near the end of one of these get-togethers he suddenly boomed, "Where the hell is that darned ship's dentist?"

I gulped down my mouthful of fudge and ran to where the Captain was holding forth. He grabbed me, threw his arm about my waist, and exclaimed, "You people don't know it, but we have the best darned dentist in the entire United States Navy!" Then he related to everyone how I had saved his tooth when he thought it should be extracted. He went on to proclaim me a dental hero! I was on top of the world, and the other officers expressed their feelings by nicknaming me "Molar!"

The Captain and I became good friends for the rest of our time at sea. Although we lived in different parts of the country after we both left the Navy, we kept in touch by mail and telephone. With each communication, the Captain assured me that "our tooth" was intact and functioning well. We last spoke in the spring of 1987, and he passed away a few weeks later at the age of 90 with "that darned tooth" still in his mouth!

Richard W. Marcus, DDS

"I'm afraid I've got some bad news."

The Prison of His Mind

It's hard to fight an enemy who has outposts in your head.

Sally Kempton

Early in my dental hygiene career, I worked with children in a dream practice with four outstanding dentists. Then, thirteen years ago, I felt a special calling to take a position in a prison dental practice serving those of God's children whom most of us would prefer to forget. Naturally, working in a prison is quite different from serving the general population. My patients all wear white clothing with a unique, six-digit identification number displayed above their shirt pockets. Their crimes range from burglary to armed robbery to murder. In addition to the results of complete physicals, medical histories, x-rays, and lab reports, their medical/dental records include psychological evaluations. Sometimes, prisoners are brought to the dental clinic in restraints such as leg irons and handcuffs under escort by one or two guards.

One of my more memorable experiences occurred not long after I began practicing in the prison. That morning the sergeant assigned to Administrative Segregation—solitary—telephoned to advise that Inmate Smith was having a bad day. The sergeant asked if I wanted to reschedule Smith for another time. I replied, "No, I don't want to reschedule Smith. I need to see him today for his periodontal care. Please arrange to have him escorted to the dental clinic in time for his appointment." In preparation for his treatment, I consulted Smith's psychological evaluation and learned he was a Vietnam veteran suffering from Delayed Shock Syndrome.

About 30 minutes later, Inmate Smith arrived—escorted by two guards. My patient was in restraints and appeared to be quite agitated. Almost as soon as I began treatment, Smith started looking over his shoulder and kept repeating, "They're coming over the hill. They're coming over the hill."

I finally rolled my stool back and got his attention. I looked him straight in the eye and asked, "How far back are they?"

He answered, "A pretty good ways."

Slowly and firmly, I said, "If you will be real still and remain absolutely quiet, I'll work very fast and we'll be gone before they get here."

He stared at me for just a moment, nodded his head, and replied, "Okay." For the next 45 minutes, Inmate Smith firmly gripped the armrests of the dental chair and didn't move a muscle or make a sound. The treatment was completed successfully and I dismissed him. On his way out the door, Smith paused, turned to me and said with visible relief, "We made it, didn't we?"

At the time, there was no doubt in my mind that Inmate Smith had just relived a terrible memory and was not really aware of his surroundings. Don't ask me to explain how I knew the difference; God just gave me the wisdom to manage the situation. On that day in 1987, Smith was unable to cooperate with prison authorities because, in the prison of his mind, he was still living in 1969—running for his life.

Later that afternoon, the sergeant and I spoke on the phone. "Did you give Inmate Smith a sedative this morning while you were treating him?"

"No," I replied, "we didn't give him anything." The sergeant then explained that Inmate Smith had been unusually quiet and calm ever since returning from the clinic.

I would like to believe that God worked a small miracle through me that day and allowed Smith a few hours of peace. I continue to practice behind bars where I know my work makes a difference, and I would not trade my job for the best private practice in the country.

Pamela J. Myers, RDH

Getting an Earful

*J*oy is the feeling of grinning inside.

Dr. Melba Colgrove, quoted in *Wealth 101*
by John Rogers and Peter McWilliams

Pregnant with our daughter Jennifer, I worked as a dental hygienist every week right up until the delivery. As my "condition" became more and more obvious, many patients offered advice regarding motherhood and proper parenting techniques.

During the first six months, I was fairly agile and maneuvered around the operatory just as I had before the pregnancy. From my seventh month on, though, it became increasingly difficult to get close to my work.

One day in my ninth month, I was scheduled to clean the teeth of a very nice older gentleman—a longtime patient. Shortly after I leaned over and began working on his mouth, he started to chuckle. Since this isn't typical patient behavior, I wasn't quite sure what to make of it. A few minutes later, the man began to chuckle again—finally bursting into full-fledged laughter. Puzzled, I put down my instruments and asked him what was so funny.

With a big grin, he said, "Your baby is kicking me in the ear."

Cindy Harker, RDH

Rich with Faith

We do well in the shelter of one another.

Irish Proverb

When I was in dental hygiene school, students had to meet many difficult requirements to qualify for graduation. One of the hardest was finding—and fully treating—a patient who was rated "Class III" in calculus. (Someone whose teeth were covered with a tremendous amount of tartar.) Finding such a patient wasn't really a problem. Getting them to come back for the four to five three-hour appointments it took to complete the entire procedure was the real challenge.

It was nearing the end of the semester; and I desperately needed one more patient who would be willing to show up for all the required appointments. Then one of my classmates told me about a homeless shelter where she was sure I could find a patient. At first, I was quite wary. I didn't think a homeless person would be very dependable. But I was desperate; so I decided to give it a chance.

I did some research and discovered that the shelter to which my classmate referred me was somewhat unusual. As long as guests followed the rules—no drinking, no drugs, and mandatory attendance at church on Sunday morning and Wednesday evening—they were allowed to stay as long as they needed. Some of the people had been there ten years; others, only a couple of days.

The morning I decided to visit the shelter, the weather was cold and dreary. The building looked as if it had once been a school. One of the first things I noticed when I got inside was the temperature. It was almost as cold in the hallways as it was outside.

At first, I was frightened. Everybody just stared at me because they knew I didn't fit in—I wasn't one of them. It took all the courage I had hidden deep inside not to run out of there. Somehow, I found my voice and plastered a smile on my face. I went up to one person after another and asked if they would like to have their teeth cleaned. Most looked at me as if I was crazy. They hardly cared if they brushed their teeth once a week much less had them professionally cleaned.

My smile was beginning to falter when a man spoke up. He appeared to be in his mid-forties, very tall and thin. He told me his name was Rodney. This man had the most wonderful blue eyes I'd ever seen. They just seemed to shine with happiness and a love for life.

Rodney quickly became excited about the prospect of having his teeth cleaned. At first this struck me as odd. Most people have no desire to go to the dentist; and *nobody* gets excited. I had Rodney sit in a chair while I pulled on a pair of disposable gloves and took a dental mirror from my bag. A quick exam revealed that he was perfect. Rodney probably had more tartar on his teeth than the rest of the people in North Carolina combined. I proceeded to tell my new patient what would be involved and all the appointments he would have to be sure to show up for. He was very agreeable to come to them all.

Rodney worked at the shelter doing odd jobs, so he could

come to the school clinic any time. We set up his first appointment for the following week. That's when it dawned on me that I'd have to pick him up myself because, of course, he didn't have a car. Every day for the rest of the week, I thought about canceling. I didn't trust a stranger in my car much less a homeless one.

Then the day of Rodney's appointment arrived. I knew I had no choice but to go. Luckily, the shelter was close to the school—only a seven-minute drive. I was quite nervous when I pulled up to the shelter. At first, I didn't see him. Mixed feelings of relief and despair tore at my heart. I parked at the curb, proceeded through the entrance, and saw him waiting for me near the door. We headed for the school. That day, instead of taking seven minutes for the drive, I made it in five.

I was nervous during the entire three-hour appointment. But by the end, I was beginning to enjoy Rodney's company. He was full of life and character—funny and charming. He was different from anyone I knew. By the second appointment, I was looking forward to seeing him again; all my fears had disappeared. I somehow knew that he would pose no threat to me.

During our final appointment, I learned everything about him. He had a sordid past—full of drugs, drinking, crime, and other things he said he wasn't proud of. He had been dropped off at the shelter ten years earlier by the police. That was when, as he says, his life truly began. In order for him to have a roof over his head, he had found it necessary to stop everything he had previously considered a normal part of life.

As the years progressed, so did his faith in God and his willingness to help others. I was intrigued by his life. I was young and had been given everything I needed. My parents were paying for my schooling, my car, my apartment—whatever I needed. I hadn't learned any of life's hard lessons firsthand.

During Rodney's treatment, I began to develop respect for

him and the others at the shelter. He introduced me to some of his friends who had been there almost as long as himself. Each person had a different story that Rodney told me about. I began to understand that these people were not what everyone I knew seemed to think they were. These homeless people were not all lazy, worthless, crazy, drunks.

Yes, some may have started out that way, but nobody gave them credit for their accomplishments and the way many of them had turned their lives around. Just because Rodney didn't have a home to call his own, or a car, or a closet full of clothes, didn't mean he wasn't rich. He was rich with all life had taught him. He was rich because he took time out to listen to people, to show his support and understanding. He was rich because he cared. Most of all, he was *rich with faith.*

Looking back, I realize that when I first visited the shelter and Rodney stood up so excited, he understood he'd be teaching me far more than how to clean a very dirty mouth. He knew he would be teaching me my first hard lessons in real life. He made me aware that I was the poor one—not him.

Stephanie Pelkey, RDH

"It's your dentist, Charlie. He says it's been five years!"

8

OVERCOMING OBSTACLES

Better to lose count while naming your blessings than to lose your blessings by counting your troubles.

Maltbie D. Babcock

Anesthesia

The memory of treating my first patient in dental school is as clear to me now as it was 23 years ago. For many dentists, memories of dental school fade into the past, and we forget the harrowing experiences we were forced to endure. There were many courses to study; projects to complete; techniques to learn; and, finally, the dreaded transition from passive dental mannequin to real-live patient. Suddenly, there was an animate body attached to those teeth, a tongue that moved with a mind of its own, saliva to contend with, and eyes peering at us from a very close distance. We needed to exude confidence when there was none, act as if we had done this procedure a hundred times before, and still pay careful attention to the details of tooth preparation that we had been taught. For the newly trained student dentist, this was overwhelming.

That day started out as any other: an early morning lecture followed by a laboratory session. The topic of the day was local anesthesia. We were to be taught to give injections to numb every different tooth in the mouth as well as every section of the jaw. We were divided up in pairs to administer injections to our lab partners. For each block injection, the instructor demonstrated the anesthesia delivery on a student "volunteer." With the needle in place, the class would approach, hold the syringe, and use our fingers to explore the bony "landmarks" we had been taught to identify in the jaw (dentists call the process "palpation"). I could feel my heart beating out of my chest in sympathy for my poor classmate on the receiving end of my quest for knowledge.

Unfortunately, I was soon to learn what this felt like first-hand as I was selected for the universally dreaded "infraorbital" injection demonstration. This injection is given in the front of the mouth to numb the front teeth and a large portion of the face. As each student came forward to push the syringe toward the bony landmark beneath my eye, I slowly felt my face getting "fatter" and increasingly numb. By the time class had ended, my face on one side was completely paralyzed, as if I had suddenly acquired a Bell's Palsy. My right eye drooped, my smile sagged, my tongue felt colossal.

It was on this same day, one hour after the marathon anesthesia session, that I was scheduled to see my first-in-my-life real patient for a filling. The numbness was not even close to wearing off as I spotted the poor 73-year-old woman in the waiting room. "Hi, Mrs. J!" I slurred as I thrust out my hand in greeting. She eyed me warily, staring at my face. I sensed her apprehension and wished to relax the situation. I smiled from one side of my mouth, smacked my face, and uttered, "Oh, don't mind this, I had some dental work done this morning!" She followed me to my operatory and I seated her comfortably in the dental chair. She was so busy staring at my face she didn't notice my trembling hands and my knocking knees due to my own anxiety of actually treating my first live patient. I was to do a white composite filling on tooth number 7, one of her front teeth.

After using my newly learned skills in anesthesia delivery, I placed the rubber dam and began to drill away. I was extremely focused on the preparation—it had to be perfect, it had to go smoothly. This was my career, my future. I was engrossed in my task—barely noticing my patient's eyes, intently and continuously staring at me, getting wider and wider by the minute. All was going great—except that I was having difficulty keeping things dry. I had my suction tip in her mouth and yet my patient's napkin was getting saturated. I constantly changed her napkin. Mrs. J sat there speechless throughout the procedure— just nodding at me dumbfounded whenever I inquired as to her wellbeing.

It wasn't until the fourth napkin change that I noticed my face beginning to tingle. What joy! The feeling was returning, the numbness wearing off. It was at that critical moment I noticed, for the first time, my own saliva running down my chin and onto Mrs. J's napkin! I had been drooling for the past hour like some overgrown teething infant.

Embarrassment doesn't come close to describing the feelings that overcame me at that moment. Suffice it to say, I quickly placed the filling while smiling all the while as if to say, "Hey, this is a normal everyday dental occurrence." I suppose I cannot blame Mrs. J for not returning for the completion of her dental treatment with me. Looking back, I'm not sure I would have been as tolerant as she was had our roles been reversed.

I have been teaching at a dental school now for almost 20 years, and I still smile when a student approaches and fearfully informs me that this is their first filling on a real patient. "Don't worry," I reassure the frightened student, "when you're finished, remind me to tell you about my first real live patient."

Rochelle G. Lindemeyer, DMD

The Introduction

If two people who love each other let a single instant wedge itself between them, it grows—it becomes a month, a year, a century; it becomes too late.

Jean Giraudoux

It was a Monday morning, and I noticed two identical last names on my afternoon dental hygiene schedule. The first patient after lunch had a woman's first name and the patient following her was a man with the same last name. Often, this means the two people are related. A husband and wife or a parent and child will sometimes schedule dental appointments together for transportation reasons if nothing else. I tried to imagine who these people were as I continued preparing for the day and temporarily forgot about them in the crush of my work.

When the afternoon rolled around, my first patient was a young woman in her late twenties. She was very pleasant, and I felt comfortable with her. Before she left, I mentioned the name of my next patient and asked if they were related. I watched with surprise as a look of pure shock passed over her face. For a moment, I regretted saying anything because she suddenly appeared to be in great distress. Standing in front of me, suspended in time, surrounded by memories, she seemed to be searching her mind for something she had lost.

After an eternal moment, she looked down at the floor and mumbled her story in a shaking voice. Indeed, she was related to the gentleman on my schedule. He was her father-in-law. Ten years before, she had married her sweetheart and they had enjoyed a happy and successful union. They were now the parents of two beautiful children. She judged her husband to be a man of many fine qualities, but one thing about him disturbed her. This one thing weighed heavily on her heart, like a wound that never quite heals.

Before she met her husband, he had had a bitter disagreement with his father. My patient didn't offer any details, and I was grateful for that. For reasons known only to themselves, father and son mutually agreed never to speak to each other again. They had both honored their agreement for more than twelve years. As a result, this woman had never met her father-in-law. Knowing only his name, she had no idea what the man looked like. To make matters worse, her father-in-law's grandchildren were growing up without him.

I saw clearly that the universe had stepped in that afternoon to offer her family an opportunity for healing. This young mother could choose to act as a mediator for her husband and his father with a simple shake of her hand, a smile, and an open heart. I suggested that I could introduce them, perhaps as I walked her to the front desk. I could also provide them with a few extra minutes to meet while I cleaned the treatment room. In quick succession, fear flashed in her eyes followed by slight hesitation and a deep sigh as she raised her head to look at me.

My patient confessed that she had spent years praying for an end to this rift, but never took any action. Her husband had made her promise to keep out of it; and she had honored his wishes. Here was an unexpected chance to move toward the answer to her prayers. She decided to take it!

It must have required great courage for her to step out into the waiting room with me. I'm certain I heard her knees knocking. The introduction was simple and straightforward. I returned to my room and prepared for my next patient, the estranged father-in-law. I waited as long as I could before seating this man, and we didn't discuss anything personal while he was in the chair. He was quiet, subdued, and contemplative. For the rest of that afternoon, I felt an extraordinary sense of exultation. I had been privileged to witness a divine appointment.

I later learned that father and son had finally resolved their differences and ended their long separation. A loving and courageous heart had prevailed and a family was healed.

Delora Gillman, RDH

A Mother's Priorities

Friendship and friendliness are dentistry's most permanent fillings.

Herbert Ely Williams, DDS

Though all of our patients are cared for in an equally high quality way, some of them just touch your heart and, as a result, you enjoy seeing them more than others. I especially remember Mrs. Jones; widowed at 44 with five children, she was by no means wealthy.

For much of their young lives, the oral health care of Mrs. Jones' children had been neglected because of enormous hospital bills incurred by her ailing husband. After her husband's death, the health care of her children became her primary concern. Over the course of several years, we provided amalgams, composites, space maintainers, and orthodontics—whatever was needed for each of those children—until, one by one, they required only routine periodic checkups.

During those years, Mrs. Jones had never been able to pay her bill in full at each appointment so we set up an installment plan. She was never late with a single payment. After each appointment, our receptionist would always ask, "When will the doctor be seeing *you*, Mrs. Jones?" "Well," she'd respond with embarrassment, "My children come first. When they're all fixed up, I'll save some money and come in myself."

It was three years before that day came. In the meantime, we had tried everything to schedule Mrs. Jones, knowing that her own oral health was suffering—but she wouldn't think of accepting a handout. We never really knew just how bad her problem was because whenever she talked, or smiled, or laughed, she would put her hand over her mouth. We could only imagine what resided on the other side.

When she had finally saved enough money to be seen, we scheduled her first appointment. As we suspected, her mouth was badly in need of dental work. But, thank goodness, she had good overall bone support so we began a restorative process that took nearly eight months to complete. At the end of each procedure, we would offer her a mirror so she could see our progress. Each time, she refused saying, "That's okay. My children have beautiful smiles and I trust you." I noticed though, that she still always kept her hand in front of her mouth—the mouth that was starting to look pretty good.

Finally, the last appointment day arrived. Two bridges, four root canals, seven crowns, and many composite fillings later, we were finished. We had worked much more quickly than Mrs. Jones was able to pay, but we constantly reminded her that we trusted her. As she approached the front desk to schedule a routine teeth cleaning and exam several months away, she thanked us with a hug, but still talked with her hand in front of her mouth.

"Mrs. Jones," I said, "come here with me." I placed my hands on each of her shoulders and guided her to a big mirror in the hall. "Smile!" I said. She smiled with her hand in front of her mouth. "No, really *smile*." I said, gently pulling her hand down. You could have heard a pin drop as our whole staff watched.

All she could say was, "I'm beautiful!" Then she started to tremble and the tears began—Mrs. Jones's tears, my tears, the receptionist's tears, the dental assistant's tears...even the dentist's tears.

Not long after that, Mrs. Jones received a letter from our office—one we had intended to send all along—that read, "We apologize for any inconvenience this may have caused, but we have accidentally overcharged you in years past. We find that not only is your $6,500 balance paid in full, but we also owe you a refund of $100 that is enclosed. P.S. Yes, you *are* beautiful!"

I suspect she knows what we did, but this was a way to protect her renewed self-esteem. Besides, we have easily recovered that amount in the more than 40 new patients she has referred to our practice. But, then, it never was about the money.

Oh, yes—one last thing. About that great dentist.... I married him five years ago and we now have a wonderful three-year-old daughter. Mrs. Jones's daughter is one of our favorite babysitters.

Cindy L. Hutcheson, CDA, FADAA, BS

Mom, You're the Best!

It all began when I was thirty-five and had recently weathered a divorce. As the single parent of two young children, I decided the time had come to re-examine my life. I realized that in addition to improving my earning ability, my self-esteem was badly in need of an overhaul. During the previous decade, I had worked in numerous dental offices where I was responsible for a variety of duties. That gave me the opportunity to develop a high regard for the role of dental hygienists as healthcare providers. I also realized that dental hygiene was a career that could provide me with a deep sense of personal accomplishment. Motivated to pursue my dream, I enrolled in the two-year program at an area college.

At first there were the typical adjustments: trying to balance responsibilities to my family, lecture and lab schedules, and finding time to study. Quite soon, I discovered that my biggest supporters were my children. Jessica was ten and Justin was six when I decided to become a dental hygienist and began my journey. As is often the case with a single parent, I spent a lot of time talking with my kids. It brings a smile to my face when I recall their concern that I turn in assignments on time, listen attentively in class, and get plenty of sleep—an impossibility, but their hearts were in the right place.

For the next two years, I managed a daily 70-mile round trip commute to school, ate what seemed like tons of macaroni and cheese with the kids, and never failed to remind myself that every moment spent on my education would be worth it.

Two years into my quest, I graduated with honors and passed both the written and practical dental hygiene board examinations. What I remember most of all at the graduation ceremony was my children's proud faces as they told me, "Mom, you're the best!" Little did they appreciate how important their words would be in giving me the strength and the drive to be the best I could be every day since then.

Soon after graduation, I secured a full-time hygiene position at a dental office in my hometown. As I became an accepted member of the staff and my love for this new profession grew, I found that sharing stories of Jessica and Justin with my patients helped them relax while I cleaned their teeth.

I felt blessed to have patients who showed interest in my children; but after a busy day at the office, I looked forward to coming home and sharing the events of my day with my kids. Around the dinner table, my children would talk about their daily activities and never fail to ask whom I had had as patients and if I still enjoyed being a dental hygienist. I confirmed that my career choice was a wise decision, and my heart would smile when I heard them say those four simple words, "Mom, you're the best!" As Jessica and Justin grew up before my eyes, I came to appreciate that they were not only my children, they had become my best friends.

Eight years after my journey began, Jessica graduated from high school and was preparing for her college career. Justin, on the other hand, was looking forward to attending our church's youth retreat, a high school show choir camp, and building up his stamina for the junior varsity cross country team that would start in the fall. As I watched them enthusiastically develop their potential, I felt God had truly blessed me with the privilege of raising two beautiful children—caring and talented individuals that filled my heart with love and joy.

But six years to the day after I started my profession as a dental hygienist, 15-year-old Justin was involved in a motorcycle accident caused by an intoxicated driver. The next day, my son was declared brain dead and life support was removed. As a result of Justin's death, I was faced with the most challenging, and ultimately the most important, decision of my life—a decision that has proven to be one of the most rewarding I've ever made.

It was Jessica who first suggested we consider organ donation. She remembered a high school classmate who had died during his senior year and was impressed that this young man's parents thought of others in their time of grief. Knowing Justin, we both felt he would want us to help and think of others, too. So in order to make a positive out of a negative situation, we chose to participate in the organ donor program. It's been comforting and healing to know that through Justin's death, he helped four other people improve the *quality* of life with the *gift* of life!

As you can imagine, this unexpected tragedy totally altered the normal routine and pattern of our daily lives. It was quickly evident that my patients' lives were touched, also. The outpouring of cards, flowers, and memorials was overwhelming; and I realized that the stories I had shared with them earlier had caused our worlds to connect. Many of the cards and letters we received reflected not only sympathy, but also support for the fact that we had participated in the donor program. Many of them thanked me for sharing stories about Justin with them during their appointments; it made my son a part of their lives as well.

These days the kind of stories I share with my patients is

different than I had originally anticipated. I now tell them about my experiences as a counselor at Camp Hope, a refuge for grieving children. I tell them about sponsoring high school students for summer show choir camps, supporting MADD (Mothers Against Drunk Drivers) and SADD (Students Against Destructive Decisions), and especially promoting the organ donor program in my state. Two years after my son's death, my prayers were answered when Jessica and I met Justin's heart recipient. It was a visual confirmation that our decision was the best one and that Justin's life and memory lives on.

Kay L. Bandle, RDH

"Please let me through, gentlemen. I'm a dental hygienist."

No Disability Here

May the Floss be with you.

Steve Hagler, DDS

Teaching little kids how to care for their teeth and gums can be a lot of fun. It can also be a great learning experience as I discovered when I was enrolled in a university dental hygiene program. As hygiene students, my classmates and I were required to provide occasional community health service. On one assignment, another student and I visited an elementary school where we made a presentation to a group of sixth graders.

Following a short lecture and demonstration, we played a little game with the children to determine what they had learned from our talk. The kids were great listeners and we all had fun.

The last thing we did was make sure they knew how to properly brush their teeth. We talked about it first and then gave each child a new toothbrush so we could all brush together. At this point, my classmate and I split the class into two groups. Working with young children, this is usually a straightforward task; but on that particular day, I faced a new challenge.

In my half of the class was a girl who had been born without arms. I was not at all sure just how to handle the situation. But as I gave each child a toothbrush, this young lady responded as all the other students did. She took the toothbrush out of the plastic wrapping and held it in position to be ready to brush. The only difference between her and the other students was that she did this with her *feet*. She was so well coordinated that she used her feet and toes just like the rest of us use our hands and fingers. I soon realized she was not going to present a challenge at all; she had everything under control. As a matter of fact, as I watched these sixth graders brush their teeth, it became apparent that this young lady had the best dexterity and did the best job in the entire group. She was very motivated to do a great job, and didn't hesitate to put her motivation into action.

After the brushing session, I discussed flossing. This young lady said she used a special floss holder and that she flossed every day. I truly believe she does; she had beautiful teeth.

When I left the school that day, I felt a little ashamed...and greatly inspired at the same time. I was ashamed of the fact that far too many of us—who have all of their body parts functioning perfectly—are just too lazy to take care of the simple tasks in life. The fact that brushing and flossing require a little bit of time and effort didn't stop this young lady. I was inspired because she had such a great attitude. She could have sulked and felt sorry for herself; but, she obviously didn't do that. Instead, she decided to work with what she had...and did it with a fantastic attitude. She did more with her two feet than most people do with two hands *and* two feet.

The memory of that young lady will forever be an inspiration to me. She has every right to be proud of herself; she has a lot to teach the world. She certainly taught me a lesson!

Leanne Rodine, RDH

A Gift from Mom

Disconcerted. I believe that's the best way to describe the look I all too often put on my mother's face. Looking back, you could say I was a problem child—and you'd be right!

You won't be surprised to learn I was a poor student, my grades were a solid D+. Nevertheless, my mom had faith in me, the kind of faith only a mother can have. Maybe it was just blind hope, or perhaps it was because I was her only child—an all-her-eggs-in-one-basket sort of thing. Throughout my young life, Mom provided constant encouragement, always trying to inspire me.

It wasn't until I was a sophomore in high school that my attitude changed. That's when I decided I wanted to become a doctor—what *every* mom dreams of for her kids, right? To help people like me, my school offered a yearlong class for juniors called "Medical Careers."

In the first academic quarter, the course provided a review of various healthcare professions and allied health careers. For the following three-quarters, students were placed in various healthcare settings such as the local hospital, or the office of a dentist or veterinarian. For some reason, the chance at some real life work experience appealed to me.

To gain admission to Medical Careers, each candidate had to prepare a short application—one or two paragraphs stating why they wanted to take the class. The good news was that grades were not considered in the selection process. Encouraged by this, I put my thoughts into a brief letter, turned it in to my guidance counselor, and was soon accepted into the class.

Soon afterward, the school sent announcements to the parents of all students accepted into the program. My mom received one of those letters. It started out, "Dear Parent(s): I am pleased to inform you that your child has been accepted into next year's Medical Careers Program." The letter went on to describe the course and was signed by the director.

The way my mom responded to the news, you'd think I'd been accepted into Harvard. She showed me the letter and told me how proud she was. In spite of my telling her how easy it was to get into the course—nobody who applied was turned down as far as I know—she was delighted. I now understand why. This was the first proof she had that there was hope for her problem child, that the faith she had in her son was not misplaced, that perhaps the hopes and dreams she had for his future would be fulfilled.

My mother died that summer. Cancer.

After the funeral, I had occasion to go through some of mom's things—including the book I'd given her the previous Christmas. Tucked within its pages was the Medical Careers Program letter.

Since my mom's death, I've never again been able to give her a birthday, Christmas, or Mother's Day gift. But any time I want a gift from my mom, all I have to do is think about that letter—carefully folded and pressed between the pages of her book.

Michael Kowalski, DDS

Happiness Is a Choice

*A happy person is not a person in a certain set
of circumstances, but rather a person with a
certain set of attitudes.*

Hugh Downs

Sometimes we learn more from our patients than we teach.
For me, that patient was Sue. Every morning, my staff and I go
through the patient list for the day. We discuss treatment preparation, supplies needed, and pertinent information for each
patient. One day while looking through the schedule, Nancy, my
office manager, noted that Sue Spandler was coming in.
"Everyone be extra nice to Sue today," Nancy said. "She's going
through a rough time. Her husband, Bill, has advanced rheuma-
toid arthritis and it has begun to affect his lungs."

"I didn't know that arthritis could affect your lungs," piped
in Ellen, my assistant.

"Yes," I answered. "The lungs need flexibility to expand and
contract so that air can flow in and out. As the arthritis pro-
gresses, the flexibility is lost. The lungs can't fill with oxygen
or squeeze out the carbon dioxide."

"Oh, she must be so sad and scared," said Ellen.

"Not just scared," said Nancy; "the poor woman must be exhausted. Bill can't stay in one position for more than a few hours without pain and stiffness. Sue has to get up several times each night to wake him and help him move around. She hasn't had a full night's sleep in months."

We all decided to spend a few extra minutes with Sue that day trying to make her comfortable and offer kind words. It is our custom to give a fresh flower to each patient as they leave. Since Sue's appointment was late in the day, we decided to give her not just one flower, but all the flowers left from the bouquet. We just wanted to do something to brighten her day.

Late in the afternoon as I looked at my schedule, I realized that Sue was my next patient. I took a deep breath and tried to steel myself for what I might find. What I expected was a woman with the joy sucked out of her…dark circles under her eyes…little care for makeup or fancy clothes. I expected the drooped posture of a person worn down by exhaustion and sadness. Imagine my surprise as I entered the operatory to find a perky, energetic woman with a broad smile on her face. She had a funky new hairstyle, bright eyes, and rosy cheeks. She wore a royal blue jacket over a crisp white blouse. Puffed around her neck was a silk scarf splashed with every color in the rainbow.

"Oh, excuse me," I mumbled as I hastily exited the room. Finding Ellen, I asked, "What happened to Sue? Did she cancel? Why wasn't the schedule updated? Who is in Room 3? Where's the new chart?"

"That is Sue, Doctor," Ellen laughed. "Go talk to her. You'll be surprised."

Confused, I walked back into the room. "Sue?" I asked, "How are you? You look wonderful."

"Hi, Doctor Teri," Sue replied, "I am excellent. Bill and I just got back from Florida. We went to Disney World and had a blast. We put a Goofy hat on his oxygen tank, stuck it in a stroller, and wheeled that thing around like proud parents! You should have seen Bill screaming through his oxygen mask as we rode down Splash Mountain. I never laughed so hard in my life. When he couldn't walk, I pushed him in a wheelchair. With the wheelchair, we were able to go to the front of every line. It was great!"

"It sounds like Bill is doing much better. That's wonderful."

"He's really not," Sue replied. "His arthritis gets worse each day. I don't know how much time he has left, but then, none of us really knows, do we?"

"Oh Sue, I'm so sorry. This must be absolutely awful for you."

"Awful?" she said, confused. "I've never been happier in my life. Every morning when I open my eyes I see the man I love next to me. I get to spend the entire day with him—something we never got to do when we were both working or the children were small. When I lie down at night with my hand resting in his, my husband's beautiful face is the last thing I see before I close my eyes. Why be sad that he's dying? I choose to be happy that he's alive."

We gave Sue the flowers when she left, all of us suddenly counting our blessings. "Life is a lot like these flowers, you know," Sue said. "*Now* is the time to enjoy the bloom! There'll be plenty of time later to lament the withering."

Teri Steinberg, DDS

Cherishing the Moment

I was busy lamenting the trials and tribulations of another turbulent day at the office when my thoughts were interrupted by a special bulletin on the television. I always tense up a little when one of those reports abruptly flashes across the screen. *What was this all about?* I wondered. *Maybe the baseball strike was settled, or maybe there was yet another twist in the O.J. Simpson case?* My thoughts were stopped cold, and I went numb as I tried to absorb what the TV was reporting. "A USAir jumbo jet, Flight 427 from Chicago, appears to have crashed on approach to the Pittsburgh airport." I shook my head as if to rid it of such a terrible thought. My head stopped shaking, and the news was still there. Things like this always happen somewhere else, not here in Pittsburgh.

Details over the next few hours confirmed my worst fears. No survivors. One hundred and thirty-two passengers and crew were dead. The cruelest fate affected a family that lived near my office whose children attended the same schools my children did. This family was returning from a funeral service for their young nephew in Chicago. The entire family—mother, father, and three children—perished in the crash. One member of this family was an 11-year-old girl. I look at my own daughter running, jumping, and laughing and wondered how in an instant this could all be taken away from someone so innocent. Little did I know that my neighbor's child would touch me emotionally in a way that I am sure will affect me my entire life.

As the reality of the disaster sank in, the magnitude of the grim task of identifying the remains of the victims took hold. The impact and devastation of the full-speed crash made recognition of any of the passengers impossible. Dentist members of the Pennsylvania Disaster Identification Team mobilized quickly. After the identification process was well under way, I was asked to volunteer in the forensic efforts to relieve the first wave of dentists who no doubt were emotionally and physically spent. I did not want to go. But somehow I felt like I had a duty to do so. I feared this would be the worst experience of my professional career. It was. I had no idea that it could have such a *positive* effect on my personal life. It did.

My apprehension for what I was about to see reduced my voice to an insecure whisper as I asked directions to the hangar where the temporary morgue was set up. I parked my car and tried to convince my legs to move in the indicated direction.

I stood at the morgue entrance nearly overcome with emotion, yet stunned by the precision with which the tasks were being performed around me. In blue scrubs and full-body protective clothing, forensic pathologists, FBI agents, anthropologists, radiology technicians, and dentists blended into a sea of blue that flowed through the different stations in the morgue. Each station had a particular function. The dental team charted identifiable oral structures with the hope of identifying the remains by matching the charted findings to antemortem dental records of the victims.

I was directed to the dental area where teams took turns cleaning and then charting the remains. Almost immediately, the icy reality of this task chilled me when one of the runners brought to us the remains of one of the victims. It was my turn.

The only portion of the remains that even had the *potential* for identification was a small fragment of a jaw about two inches in length. One of the team members directed me to dissect and clean the fragment so any recognizable dental structures could be charted. There was a bicuspid that appeared to have been intruded into the jaw during impact, a fully erupted first molar and some remnants of a second molar that also appeared to have been intruded. It was not until I examined the radiograph of the segment that it hit me. This tiny fragment revealed the most sobering news I had ever received in my life. The teeth were not intruded at all. They had not erupted yet. These were the remains of that 11-year-old girl. Holding the remains of someone whose potential to enjoy life had vanished in an instant was unbearable. I peered out at the team leader not even caring if my mask hid my tears.

The real heroes in this disaster were the dentists who, with supreme commitment—and dedication, worked tirelessly in the identification effort. I only made it for four hours. But in those four hours that little girl gave me a gift that will last my entire life. She focused my core beliefs and helped me realize that what is most precious in life is what you have *right now.* It is what you are doing *right now.* It is what you believe in *right now.* Our time here is limited. Cherish it.

God bless the victims of USAir Flight 427. God bless that little girl.

Timothy G. Donley, DDS, MSD

One Last Wish

Roger, a ten-year-old, was one of the best patients our dental team had ever been privileged to care for. His mother always accompanied him for dental appointments and explained on his first visit that her son had the AIDS virus. Afflicted with hemophilia since birth, the boy had contracted the virus from a blood transfusion.

Roger was quite small for his age. His mother explained that his slight stature was due to the heavy AIDS medications he had been forced to take for much of his young life. Roger was fully aware of how serious his illness was, but his situation was made even more difficult by the prejudice and irrational fears of some people who totally misunderstood the nature of his disease. In spite of these challenges, Roger had the greatest positive attitude of anyone I've ever known.

He came in to have his teeth cleaned regularly and always showed up with a bright, smiling face, eager to be treated just like any other patient. But we all knew Roger wasn't like any other patient we'd ever had. Not because he had AIDS, but because he had a maturity far beyond his years. This maturity allowed him to accept people—some friendly and some not-so-friendly, and circumstances—good, bad, and just plain awful, as a part of life. After every visit, we felt inspired and uplifted by his spirit—a spirit that radiated pure love.

Naturally, Roger's AIDS treatments took precedence over his dental needs. Now and then, months would pass between visits because he had to travel to major medical centers around the country for advanced procedures—some of which were experimental.

After a long quiet spell, we received a phone call one morning from Roger's mother requesting an appointment—that afternoon. We were happy to work him into the schedule.

When he arrived, it was obvious Roger had lost considerable weight since we had last seen him. The boy's skin just seemed to hang on his small, bony frame, making him look five years younger than he really was.

Roger's mother said he had made a list of the things he wanted done before he died since he and his parents knew full well the end was near. One request was to have his last primary tooth extracted as he felt he was too old to still have "baby" teeth. I brought Roger and his mother back to an operatory where I helped him into the chair and made him as comfortable as possible.

From the time Roger entered our office, he clutched a clear plastic bag to his chest. One end of a tube was connected to the bottom of the bag; the other end disappeared under his shirt just above the belt buckle. Roger's mother told me he was on a morphine drip directly into his stomach to ease severe pain due to AIDS complications.

With the help of God gained over the long years of her son's illness, his mother managed to hold herself together emotionally during the procedure. I wasn't nearly as strong and had trouble holding back the tears. For a few minutes, I had to leave the room to regain my composure; I couldn't bear to have our young patient see my distress.

It didn't take long to complete the extraction. At the end of the procedure, Roger was tired—but very happy the tooth had been removed. Soon after he left the office, everyone on the staff seemed drawn together to comfort each other as we talked about how ill he had become and realized that this was probably his last visit.

A week later, Roger's mother called to let us know her son was no longer in pain…he had died and gone to Heaven. She said that one of the things Roger asked her to do just before he passed away was thank our staff for making a major contribution to his happiness by granting one of his last wishes. A wish to have some normalcy in his life. A wish to be just like you and me.

Valerie J. Martinson

Courage

The greatest part of our happiness or misery depends on our disposition and not on our circumstances.

Martha Washington

Courage is a twelve-year-old boy named Jim. Not Jimmy, just Jim. Jim was not your typical twelve-year-old; he was going on forty. Mature well beyond his years, his outlook was probably not adopted by choice; it was dictated by circumstance. Jim had leukemia. He fully understood what that meant and the seriousness of the matter. He was the pillar of strength for his parents even though it was he whose body was wracked by this awful disease. Jim took on each day as though it might be his last. While he didn't feel sorry for himself, he didn't try to sugarcoat or deny negative possibilities either.

I met Jim and his mother when he was preparing to start treatment for his leukemia. Patients with cancer (leukemia is a form of cancer) usually see a dentist before they start chemotherapy and/or radiation treatment. This is because chemotherapy affects the immune system; and the body's ability to fight infection—including dental infection—is compromised. Similarly, radiation treatment to the head and neck can reduce healing potential in the jaws (where our teeth are rooted) as well as diminish a person's saliva, a natural protectant of the teeth.

It is never easy for me to treat cancer patients. Usually they are seeing many doctors concurrently; and besides being overwhelmed by what is going on in their bodies, they are physically fatigued by traveling from appointment to appointment. It is especially hard for me to see very young people because I remember what I was doing when I was their age. I simply cannot image the devastating impact of knowing that something very abnormal is occurring in your life instead of being focused on the usual concerns of an adolescent.

When I spoke with Jim and his mother, it was readily apparent that the boy understood everything I said. He impressed me by actually answering his mother's questions before I had the chance. When I asked if he knew why he was seeing me as part of his care, he gave a five-minute dissertation on the involvement of the mouth as a source of infection. Had he been a dental student taking an exam, he would have aced that question. He went on to explain that he'd been reading up on his disease and was doing everything in his power to beat it. As he delivered these words, I felt a profound respect for the determination of this young man while, at the same time, a good-sized lump took up residence in my throat.

Following my visits with Jim, I called his oncologist to check up on how the boy was doing. He said that actually Jim's prognosis was very good and that his type of leukemia should respond well to treatment and not prove fatal. "That kid sure is something else," the doctor said. "He was asking me questions I thought would be way over his head." I shared my similar experience, and we both agreed that Jim was going to occupy a very special place in our memories.

Each time I see Jim, I'm reminded of the life struggle he has overcome, a struggle far greater than most of us will encounter in our entire lives. "See, I told you I was going to beat it!" he proclaimed a year after his treatment ended.

"Yes, you sure did, Jim," I said. That was one of the best "I told you so's" I've ever heard. From that point on, Jim stopped focusing on his illness and started talking much more about his future, something I took as a good sign. I'm certain he'll be successful in whatever he chooses because of the positive way in which he approached his treatment and the initiative he showed in learning all he could about his disease. But even more important than that, I was impressed with how he regarded others, particularly the way he comforted his mother during that very trying time.

Whenever I face difficult decisions, I always think of Jim. It may sound silly to be attached to the memory of a twelve-year-old boy, but I can think of few better examples of how to deal with an unwanted challenge.

Stephen J. Meraw, DDS, MS

$\overline{9}$

ECLECTIC
WISDOM

Fat and Funny Water

*It is an extreme honor to be the first woman in
the United States to become a certified dentist. I
will be the first of many, I am certain.*

Lucy Hobbs Taylor, 1867

I entered pediatric dentistry with the intention of helping
children achieve a lifetime of dental health. I never expected to
be a major influence in a patient's career choice. Doing so gave
me my greatest satisfaction as a dentist.

Erica was referred to me at age four. Her first visit to a dentist
had been a traumatic experience. Subsequently, she bounced
from dentist to dentist until she was deemed unmanageable.

Pediatric dentists learn that before you can treat a child you
have to gain their trust. One technique used to accomplish this
is called "desensitization." The child is slowly exposed to
increasingly stronger stimuli as time goes on.

At our first meeting, Erica hid behind her mother and
refused to look at me. I sat on the edge of my dental chair and
spoke to her softly. I asked how old she was and if she were
married or had a boyfriend. With those questions, she looked at
me from behind her mother's skirt with an expression that said,

"Is this man a nut?"

I then asked Erica if she knew how to count. I told her I loved to count but that I sometimes needed help. I took her hand and started counting her fingers—making a few mistakes so she could correct me. I continued to count her eyes, ears, nose and belly button, a process that evoked a big smile.

I asked her how many teeth she had. She said she didn't know. I gave her a mirror to watch while I counted her teeth with my fingers. I told her it was hard for me to count this way. Could she sit in the chair? She climbed into the chair hesitantly and allowed me to count her teeth. I told her it was still hard for me to count her teeth. Could I use my little mirror? I showed her my mirror and counted her fingers, eyes, ears, nose, belly button, and teeth. I repeated the routine with my dental explorer—a metal probe introduced to patients as a "tooth counter." She cooperated for x-rays of her teeth. The radiographs revealed an exposed nerve that demanded immediate performance of a child's root canal.

A local anesthetic—the dreaded needle—was necessary. I explained to Erica that I was going to wash some "dirt" out of her tooth, but first I was going to put her tooth to sleep and make her lip feel "fat and funny." I gave her a little mirror so she could watch me spray the water behind the tooth. I sprayed some anesthetic on her hand. I told her the water was cold so she might feel a little pinch, but if she watched the little red button—the rubber stopper on the anesthetic cartridge—the cold pinch would warm up and go away. She sat for the anesthetic without a flinch and I successfully treated her tooth.

Over the next few weeks, I restored the rest of her teeth, each time using the fat and funny water. Erica returned for periodic checkups and usually had one or two cavities that needed treatment until age nine. Then she started losing her baby teeth and her adult teeth appeared. From that point on, she remained cavity free and no longer required the fat and funny water. She left my practice at age eighteen when she entered college.

The next time I saw Erica was eight years later. While attending college, she had decided to become a dentist. She completed dental school and had begun her residency at the hospital where I was on staff. When she saw me, she excitedly related the following story.

In her second year of dental school, the students learned local anesthesia technique by practicing on each other. With much trepidation, she waited for her classmate to inject her. Eyes closed, she prepared herself for the excruciating pain felt when receiving an injection. Instead she noticed a cold water pinch and then her lip began to tingle and feel funny. It was at that moment she realized—for the first time in her life—that my "fat and funny water" she experienced throughout her dental treatment was the dreaded injection. She ran around the clinic shouting, "I can't believe that's the 'fat and funny water'." This revelation impressed her so, she decided to become a pediatric dentist. After completing her general practice residency, she continued on to postgraduate training in pediatric dentistry.

The story doesn't end there. On her first day of postgraduate training, an instructor approached and explained to Erica that there was a very anxious little girl waiting with a toothache. Her instructor realized Erica hadn't received any formal training in dealing with an apprehensive child, but he told her she should try her best to calm the patient and at least perform an examination.

Erica sat with the patient and repeated a scenario in which she herself had participated twenty years earlier. The instructor watched Erica talk to the patient, count her fingers, eyes, ears, nose, belly button, and teeth. He observed her take x-rays, anesthetize the child with "fat and funny water," and successfully provide the required treatment. Amazed at her abilities, the instructor asked, "Where did you learn that?"

Erica replied, "From my dentist, Dr. Steve Schwartz."

The instructor broke out in a grin. "I should have realized that. Dr. Schwartz was my junior resident. I taught him everything he knows. There's not much more I need to teach you," he said and offered her a position in his private practice.

Steven Schwartz, DDS

A Bridge for Mother-in-Law

I don't have false teeth! Do you think I'd buy
teeth like these?

Carole Burnett

For some time I had planned on trying out a new, highly recommended dental laboratory. Finally, the opportunity presented
itself. My patient had a long appointment on Thursday morning.
I prepared eight teeth for crowns and sent her impressions to the
lab. I asked for the gold work to be ready for a try-in one week
later.

On Monday morning, a very irate dental technician called
and demanded to speak to me. Furious, he inquired, "How can
you possibly expect me to have this case ready by Thursday? I'll
need at least two weeks!"

"Two weeks?" I gasped.

"At least!" he screamed. "I have to pour the models, trim the
dyes, cast the gold, and fit the copings!" He went on for several
minutes.

I tried, unsuccessfully, to interrupt his angry tirade. When
he was finally exhausted, I asked softly, "Are you married?"

The overwrought technician snapped, "Yes! What does that have to do with anything?"

I explained—gently—that this case was for my mother-in-law, that she lived in Florida, and that she had come to stay at my house in New York until her bridge was finished. I told the technician that if I could try in her gold this Thursday, we could seat her porcelain crowns by the following Thursday, and she could be back in her Florida condo by that weekend.

There was a pause on the other end of the line. Finally, the technician spoke into the silence. "Do you need it Thursday *morning* or Thursday *afternoon*?"

Jeffrey M. Galler, DDS

*"No, Dr. Bella, you cannot deduct
'expenses for wiring your mother-in-law's mouth shut'
under Home Improvement."*

Country Dentist

Bargain hunting? Beware of bargains in para-chutes, fire extinguishers, life preservers, brain surgery, and dental care.

Author Unknown

My father was a country dentist, a professional man not unlike the country doctors of the 19th and early 20th centuries. He earned the Doctor of Dental Surgery degree at the Chicago School of Dentistry in 1919 and opened his own practice in western Minnesota a few weeks before his 21st birthday.

For the next 42 years, he served the community by filling teeth, performing extractions, and doing much of his own lab work for crowns and bridges. During his entire career as a small town dentist, he never sent a bill. "If they can pay, they will," he said of his patients. A slab of home-cured bacon or a couple of dressed chickens were acceptable barter for dental work done. The farmers—and most of them were farmers—usually came to settle up in the fall after the crop was sold. Sometimes the bill for the year's work for the farmer, his wife, and three children would be around $40. My father would say, "Thirty dollars will be fine." Seldom did he accept the full amount due.

During the Depression years, it became increasingly difficult for people to pay their bills. Arthur Bolstad was one of the patients bothered by his mounting dental bill for his wife, son, and daughter. He approached my father in 1932 with the proposition that he deliver eggs from their farm to our house every Saturday until the bill was paid. My father agreed to the idea, but asked the Bolstads keep a tally on it.

Thus began the weekly routine of the Bolstads delivering eggs. The Whitneys and the Grieblers also wanted the eggs. Deliveries were made to the Whitney's back-porch, and each Saturday afternoon it was my job to pick up the three or four dozen for our family's weekly needs. Mrs. Bolstad penciled the bill in her fine handwriting on a piece of lined tablet paper. Her record might indicate:

July 23, 1934, 3 doz. eggs, at 8 cents a dozen = $.24

The price varied from seven or eight cents a dozen to 15 cents a dozen, depending on year-to-year inflation and seasonal market conditions.

The Bolstad eggs, a permanent part of our diet, were delivered without fail every Saturday for years...and years...and years. The Bolstads continued to have dental work done and Mrs. Bolstad continued to keep the books.

In the spring of 1943, Mr. Bolstad called on my father late on a Friday afternoon just as the office was closing. He shuffled his feet and turned his feed cap 'round and 'round in his hands. Whatever he had on his mind was embarrassing to him. Finally he stammered, "Doc, would you like to settle up for the eggs?"

"Why, of course," answered my father. "How much do you owe me?"

"Well...." There was a pause. *"You owe me $200!"*

Jane A. Soli

Prayer of the Dental Hygienist

Lord, open my heart
To accept all people I meet today
With an equal attitude of caring and concern.

Strengthen my character,
That I may not be afraid
To display the courage of my convictions.

Guide my hands,
So that the skills I have acquired
May give my patients better health.

Touch my spirit,
So those who come to me in need
May leave happier and healthier
For having been in my care.

Amen

Sandy Westenberger, RDH

The Dentist's Prayer

Thank you O Lord,
For the privilege of being a dentist.

For letting me serve as Your instrument
In ministering to the sick and afflicted.

May I always treat with reverence
The human life which You have brought into being,
And which I serve.

Deepen my love for people
So that I will always give myself gladly and generously
To those stricken with illness and pain.

Help me to listen patiently,
Diagnose carefully,
Prescribe conscientiously,
And treat gently.

Teach me to blend gentleness with skill,
To be a dentist with a heart as well as a mind.

Amen

Joseph G. Kalil, DDS

More Chicken Soup?

Many of the stories and poems you have read in this book were submitted by readers like you who had read earlier *Chicken Soup for the Soul* books. We are planning to publish five or six *Chicken Soup for the Soul* books every year. We invite you to contribute a story to one of these future volumes.

Stories may be up to 1,200 words and must uplift or inspire. You may submit an original piece or something you clip out of the local newspaper, a magazine, a church bulletin or a company newsletter. It could also be your favorite quotation you've put on your refrigerator door or a personal experience that has touched you deeply.

To obtain a copy of our submission guidelines and a listing of upcoming *Chicken Soup* books, please write, fax, or check one of our Web sites.

Chicken Soup for the *(Specify Which Edition)* Soul
P.O. Box 30880 • Santa Barbara, CA 93130
fax: 805-563-2945
Web site: *chickensoup.com*

You can also visit the *Chicken Soup for the Soul* site on America Online at keyword: chickensoup.

Just send a copy of your stories and other pieces, indicating which edition they are for, to any of the above addresses.

We will be sure that both you and the author are credited for your submission.

For information about speaking engagements, other books, audiotapes, workshops and training programs, please contact any of the authors directly.

Supporting Children and Families

In the spirit of fostering more love in the world, a portion of the proceeds from sales of *Chicken Soup for the Dental Soul* will go to the **Samuel D. Harris Fund for Children's Dental Health**, a permanent endowment fund of the ADA Health Foundation. The primary objective of this program is the prevention of tooth decay and other oral diseases in children, particularly for those children whose economic status places them at greatest risk of not receiving adequate oral health education and access to preventive care.

The ADA Health Foundation is the leading national charitable organization with the primary focus of enhancing clinical dentistry and, in turn, the oral health of the American public. It accomplishes this central mission by providing funds—gathered from grants, government agencies, and private contributions—for charitable projects, awareness activities, and basic and applied dental research and educational programs.

Because of its strategic ties with the American Dental Association, the ADA Health Foundation's ability to advance clinical dentistry is greatly strengthened. Funding is provided to a wide range of philanthropic programs aimed at improving dentistry's understanding of oral diseases and increasing both access to and quality of dental care for all populations. By fostering continuous advancement in dental research, education and access, the Foundation significantly impacts the oral health of the public and the practice of dentistry.

ADA Health Foundation
Samuel D. Harris Fund for Children's Dental Health
211 E. Chicago Avenue
Chicago, Illinois 60611
phone: 312-440-2547
fax: 312-440-3526
email: adahf@ada.org

Who Is Jack Canfield?

Jack Canfield is one of America's leading experts in the development of human potential and personal effectiveness. He is both a dynamic, entertaining speaker and a highly sought-after trainer. Jack has a wonderful ability to inform and inspire audiences toward increased levels of self-esteem and peak performance.

He is the author and narrator of several bestselling audio- and videocassette programs, including *Self-Esteem and Peak Performance, How to Build High Self-Esteem, Self-Esteem in the Classroom* and *Chicken Soup for the Soul—Live.* He is regularly seen on television shows such as *Good Morning America, 20/20* and *NBC Nightly News.* Jack has coauthored numerous books, including the *Chicken Soup for the Soul* series, *Dare to Win* and *The Aladdin Factor* (all with Mark Victor Hansen), *100 Ways to Build Self-Concept in the Classroom* (with Harold C. Wells) and *Heart at Work* (with Jacqueline Miller).

Jack is a regularly featured speaker for professional associations, school districts, government agencies, churches, hospitals, sales organizations and corporations. His clients have included the American Dental Association, the American Management Association, AT&T, Campbell Soup, Clairol, Domino's Pizza, GE, ITT, Hartford Insurance, Johnson & Johnson, the Million Dollar Roundtable, NCR, New England Telephone, Re/Max, Scott Paper, TRW and Virgin Records. Jack is also on the faculty of Income Builders International, a school for entrepreneurs.

Jack conducts an annual eight-day Training of Trainers program in the areas of self-esteem and peak performance. It attracts educators, counselors, parenting trainers, corporate trainers, professional speakers, ministers and others interested in developing their speaking and seminar-leading skills.

For further information about Jack's books, tapes and training programs, or to schedule him for a presentation, please contact:

Self-Esteem Seminars
P.O. Box 30880 • Santa Barbara, CA 93130
phone: 805-563-2935 • fax: 805-563-2945
Web site: *www..chickensoup.com*

Who Is Mark Victor Hansen?

Mark Victor Hansen is a professional speaker who, in the last twenty years, has made over four thousand presentations to more than 2 million people in thirty-two countries. His presentations cover sales excellence and strategies; personal empowerment and development; and how to triple your income and double your time off.

Mark has spent a lifetime dedicated to his mission of making a profound and positive difference in people's lives. Throughout his career, he has inspired hundreds of thousands of people to create a more powerful and purposeful future for themselves while stimulating the sale of billions of dollars worth of goods and services.

Mark is a prolific writer and has authored *Future Diary, How to Achieve Total Prosperity* and *The Miracle of Tithing.* He is coauthor of the *Chicken Soup for the Soul* series, *Dare to Win* and *The Aladdin Factor* (all with Jack Canfield) and *The Master Motivator* (with Joe Batten).

Mark has also produced a complete library of personal empowerment audio- and videocassette programs that have enabled his listeners to recognize and use their innate abilities in their business and personal lives. His message has made him a popular television and radio personality, with appearances on ABC, NBC, CBS, HBO, PBS and CNN. He has also appeared on the cover of numerous magazines, including *Success, Entrepreneur* and *Changes.*

Mark is a big man with a heart and spirit to match—an inspiration to all who seek to better themselves.

For further information about Mark write:

MVH & Associates
P.O. Box 7665
Newport Beach, CA 92658
phone: 714-759-9304 or 800-433-2314
fax: 714-722-6912
Web site: *www..chickensoup.com*

Who Is Don Dible?

In his long career as an entrepreneur and consultant, Don has produced more than 10,000 seminars and dozens of conferences. He has more than a decade of experience as a seminar and conference speaker and has worked with hundreds of trade and professional associations and universities. He has been a guest lecturer at Stanford University's Graduate School of Business and the University of Pennsylvania's Wharton School.

Don has also had extensive experience in the self-help publishing industry and sold one of his companies to Prentice Hall. His first book, *Up Your OWN Organization!*, was adopted by more than 150 universities. One of his companies published a twelve-volume anthology of inspirational and self-help messages titled *Build a Better You—Starting Now!* that sold tens of thousands of copies. And he published *Chicken Soup for the Soul* coauthor Mark Victor Hansen's first book, *Future Diary*, almost 20 years ago.

Because of his extensive knowledge of the publishing industry, his experience as the author/editor/compiler of more than two dozen books, his ability to work quickly and effectively with professional associations outside his own specialty areas, and his more than 60 years' experience as a model dental patient, the *Chicken Soup* organization asked Don to serve as coauthor of *Chicken Soup for the Dental Soul*. In just six months, he persuaded more than 150 dental newsletters, bulletins, journals and magazines with a combined circulation of more than 450,000 dental professionals to help publicize his call for stories for this book. Soon afterward, he received more than 1,200 submissions from which the contents of *Chicken Soup for the Dental Soul* were selected.

To schedule Don for a presentation at your conference or meeting, please contact:

Dible Associates
1250 Oakmead Parkway, Suite 210
Sunnyvale, CA 94086
phone: 408-739-4020 • fax: 408-720-0624
email: dentalsoul@aol.com

Contributors

Luz Abrera-Crum, DDS, graduated from the USC School of Dentistry in 1987. She is a member of the American Dental Association and practices general dentistry with Yolanda Bautista, Dental Assistant, and Gaby Bautista, treatment coordinator. The nursing home in her story, "Body and Soul," is Mary Health of the Sick. She is married to James Crum and they have two children, Christine and Aurora. Dr. Abrera-Crum can be reached at LAbreraDDS@aol.com.

Kay L. Bandle, RDH, works at The Gentle Dental Emporium with Kenneth M. Bero, Jr., DDS, and his wonderful staff. She and her husband, Fred, live in West Bend, Wisconsin. She has a daughter, Jessica Bobholz, and two step-daughters, Katrina and Daisy Bandle. She takes this opportunity to dedicate her story, "Mom, You're the Best!" to the memory of her son, Justin Bobholz (June 20, 1981 to July 4, 1996) and to Slinger High School, Class of 1999.

Josette Beach, RDH, MS, has been a dental hygienist for the past 21 years. During this time, she has had the pleasure of working in the practice of a kind and compassionate Portland, Oregon dentist, Shoun Ishikawa, DMD. For the last four years, she has been a full time dental hygiene instructor and clinic coordinator at the Portland Community College while continuing to work as a dental hygienist in private practice.

Ken Berg is the former editor of a medium-sized daily newspaper, *The Free Press*, published in Mankato, Minnesota. Although now retired, he continues to write a column of local interest for the paper. In Ken Berg's story, "The Christmas Gift," the out of town visitor from Connecticut coping with a painful predicament on Christmas Eve is Ken's own brother-in-law, Patrick Bresnan.

Laurence M. Brownstein, DDS, graduated from dental school in 1985 and spent the first two years of practice volunteering his dental skills for the grassroots organization of SERVOL on the Caribbean island of Trinidad. He currently practices with his father in Sausalito, California, and is an Associate Professor at the University of the Pacific School of Dentistry one day a week.

Eric K. Curtis, DDS, MAGD, has written a book and more than 250 articles about dentistry. A University of the Pacific School of Dentistry graduate, Fellow of the American College of Dentists, and Master of the Academy of

General Dentistry, he was the Arizona Dental Association's 1999 "Dentist of the Year." Dr. Curtis practices in Safford, Arizona.

Ellen Dietz, CDA, BS, is self-employed and a licensed Arizona business owner. She has published six books on dentistry and has written numerous dental articles, newsletters, and accredited continuing dental education courses. She provides freelance copywriting services for dental healthcare professionals and can be reached at her company, DentEssentials, at 480-890-2641.

Timothy G. Donley, DDS, MSD, was born, raised, and then practiced in Pittsburgh, Pennsylvania for ten years before relocating to Bowling Green, Kentucky. He graduated from the University of Notre Dame and Georgetown University School of Dentistry, and completed his specialty training at the Indiana University Medical Center in Indianapolis. Currently, he practices periodontics and dental implantology. He also lectures and publishes frequently on topics of interest to clinical dentists. Dr. Donley recommends brushing, flossing, and *Chicken Soup for the Dental Soul* to all of his patients!

MJ Endres is known for conducting workshops that rekindle the spirit in the workplace and personal life. She has led medical and dental workshops internationally. She delivers customized seminars on creativity, communication, individual and team learning, performance skills enhancement, leadership, virtual teams, and change management. She can be reached via email at MJEndres@texas.net. You may also reach MJ at Performance Mastery, 2901 Niagara Drive, Austin, Texas 78733 or by phoning 512-263-9744.

Jeffrey M. Galler, DDS, MAGD, lectures frequently at dental meetings, has authored articles in various dental journals, and holds patents in the field of restorative and cosmetic dentistry. In July, 1999, he received the award of Master in the Academy of General Dentistry. Dr. Galler maintains a private practice in Brooklyn, New York.

Alan H. Gelbert, DDS, FAGD, is a graduate of the University of Connecticut and received his dental degree in 1955 from the University of Pennsylvania Dental School. He is a past president of the New Haven Dental Association and past chairman of the Council on Dental Health of the Connecticut State Dental Association. In 1980, he was elected as a Fellow of the Academy of General Dentistry and retired in March, 1999. Dr. Gelbert resides at 186 Crestwood Terrace, Orange, Connecticut 06477 and may be contacted by phone at 203-795-3824.

Danny Gerstner, DDS, graduated from the Louisiana State University Dental School in 1997. He lives in Louisiana with Shirley, his wife of 22 years, and sons Jason and Eric. Dr. Gerstner's general dentistry practice is located at 5622 Jefferson Highway, Harahan, Louisiana, 70123 and he may be reached by calling 504-733-7218.

Delorah Gillman, RDH, spent the first 20 years of her life as a Navy dependent. She has an adult son who was born with spina bifida. She and her husband enjoy the pursuit of their passion—subsistence gardening—in the beautiful Commonwealth of Virginia.

Randy Glasbergen has had more than 25,000 of his cartoons published in magazines, books and greeting cards around the world. He also creates *The Better Half* which is syndicated to newspapers by King Feature Syndicate. You can find more of Randy's cartoons online at *www.glasbergen.com.*

Michael C. Goldman, DDS, graduated from the University of Maryland Dental School in 1969 after attending Clark University. His general practice—operated from a home-office—focuses on holistic and cosmetic dentistry. You may contact Dr. Goldman at 3815 East-West Highway, Chevy Chase, Maryland 20815, by phone at 301-656-6171, by fax at 301-656-4350, by email at goldentist@aol.com, or you may visit his website at *www.mgoldmandds.com.*

Adrienne Gonzales, RDH, is a lifelong resident of Henderson, Nevada. She graduated from Loma Linda University with a BS in dental hygiene in 1984. She's been blessed to work for Blair R. Hale, DMD, for the past 15 years. Her husband, Reno, and her two daughters, Alexa and Michaela, are the loves of her life.

Oscar Goren, DMD, has been loving the practice of dentistry for more than 20 years. Dealing with highly anxious patients is a daily challenge that he enjoys. He is convinced that the stress of modern society is causing an epidemic of tooth breakage and loosening of teeth due to rampant grinding of teeth and clenching of jaws. He has been very successful at helping his patients become aware of their physical stress and teaching them how to physically relax in a world of so much mental stress. He can be reached by email at zayman@aol.com or by phone at 215-332-5259.

Michael H. Halasz, DDS, graduated from Ohio State University in 1991 and has been in private practice ever since. He is married and has two wonderful children. He serves on the board of directors of the Dayton Dental Society and is an alternate delegate to the Ohio Dental Association annual meeting. He loves golf and performs standup comedy. Dr. Halasz may be contacted by phone at his Kettering, Ohio practice at 937-298-9028.

Merritt D. Halem, DDS, was educated at the New York University College of Dentistry and in 1969 completed his residency in general dentistry at the Mt. Sinai Hospital in Miami Beach. He spent six years in the U.S. Army Reserve and is now in private practice in North Miami Beach. He currently serves as an Assistant Professor for Treatment Planning and Oral Diagnosis at the Mt. Sinai Hospital. Dr. Halem is Chairman of the Olympic Village for Special Olympics for the North Miami Beach Optimists Club.

Cindy Harker, RDH, graduated from Idaho State University and has worked for 18 very rewarding years as a dental hygienist. She currently practices in the Portland, Oregon area. Cindy is a wife and mother and has been blessed with a wonderful family and great friends.

Gary E. Heyamoto, DDS, FAGD, is a 1980 graduate of the University of Washington School of Dentistry. He is a Fellow in the Academy of General Dentistry and is currently president of the Emerald City (R.V. Tucker) Cast Gold Study Club. He lives in Woodinville with his wife, Cynthia, and their two children, Tyler and Taryn. He serves as a team statistician for both the NFL Seattle Seahawks and the PAC-10 Washington Husky football team. Dr. Heyamoto practices family dentistry in Bothell, Washington and can be reached by phone at 425-485-8885.

Diane Hill, CDA, was born in Montreal, Quebec, Canada in 1950 and moved to the U.S. when she was seven. At eighteen, she married her first husband, had four children, and was divorced after 16 years of marriage. She remarried in 1988, now has six grandchildren, and feels very blessed. She has worked as a dental assistant for Dr. Van Emon for more than 20 years. Ms. Hill accepted Jesus as her personal savior in 1979.

Cindy Hutcheson, CDA, COA, CDPMA, COMSA, FADAA, BS, is an international speaker and clinical consultant. She conducts 1/2-, 1-, and 2-day participation courses and has written three books: *Attitude & the Dental Team, Clinical Dental Assisting: A Workbook Series,* and *Dental Letters & Forms for Every Practice.* Ms. Hutcheson may be reached at 2611 Promenade Parkway, Midlothian, Virginia 23113, by phone at 888-99-DENTAL, by fax at 804-794-7974, or by email at clhutch123@aol.com.

Shari Jay, RDH, a graduate of the University of Hawaii, is a practicing dental hygienist living her dream. She is blessed with two lovely daughters, Robyn and Wendy, and a beautiful granddaughter, Kailualani. She has served her profession as president of the Southern California and West Hawaii Dental Hygienists' Associations. Shari may be reached at 75-252 Nani Kailua Drive, #45, Kailua-Kona, Hawaii 96740 or by phone at 808-334-1569.

John J. Johnson, DDS, just celebrated his second year of dental practice in the Lewiston Orchards. With his office located just a few miles from the historic Snake and Clearwater Rivers, he has enjoyed treating the people of the area immensely and looks forward to many more years of general practice in this beautiful part of Idaho.

Joseph G. Kalil, DDS, is a past president of the Massachusetts Dental Society. In October of 1991, the House of Delegates of the American Dental Association accepted "The Dentist's Prayer" as the Primary Parameter of Care. It is available through the ADA catalog of saleable materials. Dr. Kalil conducts his dental practice from offices in the Methuen Professional Center, 91 Jackson Street, Methuen, Massachusetts 01844. He may be reached by phone at 978-688-1895, by fax at 978-685-0134, or on the Internet at www.DRJKALIL@NETWAY.COM.

Julie Karnazes, DDS, graduated with honors from the University of the Pacific School of Dentistry. She is the recipient of the prestigious Louis C. Ball Award for outstanding leadership and service. Julie lives and practices in San Francisco. In addition to her passion for dentistry, she is a dedicated wife and mother. Dr. Karnazes's practice is located at Four Embarcadero Center, San Francisco, California 94111 and she may be reached by calling 415-576-9800 or on the Internet at www.4dental.com.

Charles W. Kenney, DDS, completed his pre-dental education at the University of Kentucky, his dental education at Baylor University, and his orthodontic education at Indiana University. He has conducted a private orthodontics practice in Lexington, Kentucky since 1966. He and his wife, Jane, have four grown children, Gay, Mike, Pat, and Ben. Dr. Kenney is an active member of the Episcopal church, has participated in three short term dental missions in the Caribbean, and is an aspiring author.

Ira M. Klemons, DDS, PhD, is Director of the Center for Head and Facial Pain. His practice has been devoted exclusively to head and facial pain and temporomandibular joint (TMJ) disorders for more than 20 years. He is President of the American Board of Head, Neck, and Facial Pain and has lectured at medical and dental schools around the world. Additional information may be obtained on the Internet at www.headaches.com. Dr. Klemons may also be contacted at 2045 Route 35 South, South Amboy, New Jersey 08859 or by phone at 732-727-5000.

Michael Kowalski, DDS, JD, obtained his undergraduate degree from San Francisco State University, his dental degree from the University of California at San Francisco, and his law degree from Santa Clara University.

While in private practice as a general dentist, Dr. Kowalski had a particular interest in treating patients with HIV disease and was commended by a Resolution from Alameda County for his efforts. Dr. Kowalski is now with the law firm of Bradley, Curley, Asiano & McCarthy, located in San Francisco, where he represents health care professionals.

Sol Kutler, DDS, has been active in civic, community, professional, and religious work all his life. Since 1973, he has provided extensive volunteer service in many underdeveloped countries. He has received numerous honors including certificates of recognition from the ADA and Presidential citations from Rotary International where he was a finalist for the "Better World Understanding" award (granted to Pope John Paul II) and recipient of a "Humanitarian of the Year" award. You may contact Dr. Sol Kutler's Dental Health Center at 7337 Farnam Street, Omaha, Nebraska 68114 or call 402-397-2323.

Rochelle G. Lindemeyer, DMD, is Director of the Pediatric Dentistry Division at the Temple University School of Dentistry in Philadelphia, Pennsylvania. She is Board Certified by the American Academy of Pediatric Dentistry and is a Fellow of the Pierre Fauchard Academy and the International College of Dentists. Dr. Lindemeyer is currently taking woodworking classes at the University of the Arts in Philadelphia. Other hobbies include softball, barbecuing, and waverunning at the shore.

Armand A. Lugassy, DDS, PhD, has pursued a dual career: one as an educator and researcher in the field of dental materials and fixed prosthodontics, the other as a general dentist in the San Francisco Bay Area. His cartoons were specially created during his tenure as editor of the *Marin County Dental Society Newsletter*.

Richard W. Marcus, DDS, was raised in Plainfield, New Jersey, graduated from Cornell University in 1951, the University of Pennsylvania, School of Dental Medicine in 1955, and served in the U.S. Navy Dental Corps. from 1955 to 1957. He holds Certificates in Periodontics from the New York University College of Dentistry and the Manhattan Veterans Administration Medical Center. He practiced periodontics in Plainfield, New Jersey from 1961 to 1978 and in New York City from 1978 to 1990 at which time he retired and now lives in San Diego, California.

Michael Maroon, DMD, FAGD, is a 1986 graduate of the Tufts University School of Dental Medicine. Editor and publisher of "The Dental Leader" newsletter and co-founder of genR8Tnext, he provides educational seminars for other dentists around the country and is internationally recognized for his work in Functional Esthetic Dentistry. Dr. Maroon may be reached at

39 Webster Square Road, Berlin, Connecticut 06037, by phone at 860-828-3933, or via email at dentalldr@aol.com.

Valerie J. Martinson is a dental assistant in a private dental practice in Puyallup, Washington where she has practiced for eight and a half years—obviously a great place to work. Married to her high school sweetheart, she and her husband have three sons and a daughter-in-law.

J.D. Matthews, DDS, MS, earned his master's degree in foods and nutrition from Kansas State University and his doctorate from the University of Missouri at Kansas City. He served as a dentist in the U.S. Navy for three years. The son of a dentist (his father is still in practice after 40 years), he has practiced general dentistry for 16 years. Dr. Matthews and his wife, Jane, have two children, Joseph, 15, and Elise, 13, whom they teach at home.

Gregory V. McGowan, DDS, graduated from the Indiana University School of Dentistry in 1985 and has been in private practice as a general dentist in Mooresville, Indiana for 13 years. He is the dedicated father of four children and enjoys participating in many of their sports activities. Dr. McGowan is a church organist, an avid runner, and a Divemaster scuba diver.

Stephen J. Meraw, DDS, MS, is a graduate of the University of Detroit Mercy School of Dentistry. Following dental school, he completed a residence in hospital dentistry at the Johns Hopkins Hospital and is currently completing specialty training in periodontics at the Mayo Clinic. He has also served as a dental volunteer to underserved populations in Honduras and Belize.

Dennis J. Michaelson, DMD, MS, is a graduate of Utah State University and Washington University in St. Louis. He has served twice as president of the Idaho State Orthodontic Society, is a Diplomate of the American Board of Orthodontics, and cofounder of STERI-SMART, a company that provides the world's most efficient dental sterilization systems. Dr. Michaelson may be reached at 2271 Overland Avenue, Burley, Idaho 83318, or by phone toll-free at 1-877-783-7435.

Pamela J. Myers, RDH, 47, began her career as a dental assistant before becoming a hygienist. For the last 25 years, she has practiced dental hygiene full time. She and her husband of 30 years have two wonderful children. Their son, Chase, is in the U.S. Marine Reserves and works full time while their daughter, Katy, manages a small country grocery owned by Pamela and her husband. Pamela takes this opportunity to dedicate "The Prison of His Mind" to the fond memory of Esperance and Jim Cooper, her aunt and uncle, who listened to her stories and encouraged her to write them down.

Jim S. Park, DDS, completed undergraduate studies at the University of California at San Diego and graduate studies at the New York University College of Dentistry. He divides his time between New York City and Los Angeles and is currently a first year dental resident at the Wyckoff Heights Medical Center. His plans for the year 2000 include chief residency in dentistry at the New York Hospital at Queens and private practice.

Norman A. Patterson, DDS, graduated from St. Louis University Dental School in 1966 and then pursued an internship that followed postgraduate work in pediatric dentistry at Children's Hospital in Kansas City. In 1978, he responded to a church mission call and spent the next ten years in Africa with his family. He has operated a private dental practice since returning to the U.S. Dr. Patterson may be reached at 320 South Santa Fe, Fountain, Colorado 80817, by phone at 719-382-5500, or by email at NormPDent@aol.com.

Susan Paurazas, DDS, MHSA, MS, recently completed her graduate training in endodontics and practices in Michigan. Dr. Paurazas is an author and her works of poetry were recently published in an anthology of poetry and short stories titled, *Up from the Soles of Our Feet,* which is available at amazon.com.

Stephanie Pelkey, RDH, lives in Raleigh, North Carolina where she enjoys her career as a hygienist and her hobby as a writer.

Jackie S. Perry, RDH, worked as a dental assistant for two years before attending the Old Dominion University's Dental Hygiene Program from which she graduated in 1973. Ms. Perry spent almost 30 years in general dentistry practices serving patients ranging in age from two to 98—a fact that made each day interesting and different.

Deborah Goldberg Polay, RDH, received her BA in English & Communications from the University of Miami and continued her education at the University of Pennsylvania for her dental hygiene certificate. For the past 13 years, she has practiced dental hygiene with Dr. Neal Hammer in Freehold, New Jersey where she lives with her husband and son. Debbie loves tennis, reading, running, and the beach—but most of all, she loves her family!

Michelle M. Powers, RDH, a Tennessee resident, was a Certified Dental Assistant before becoming a Registered Dental Hygienist. She is getting married to a wonderful man in November 1999 and feels lucky to have been blessed with a wonderful family, friends, and coworkers. You may contact Ms. Powers by email at mpblueeyes@aol.com.

Robert Quintano, DDS, is a musician at the Living Branch Church in Conroe, Texas. To put food on the table, he also serves as the dental director of a large dental clinic in Conroe. He is a graduate of Cornell University and the University of Texas Health Science Center at San Antonio. After seven years of private practice in coastal North Carolina, he moved back to Texas to help raise his grandbabies, Kaitlyn and Sarah. You may reach Dr. Quintano at bobq@mcia.com.

Leanne Rodine, RDH, is currently employed by the Calgary Regional Health Authority as a community health dental hygienist in Calgary, Alberta. She spent six great years in private practice before going into community health and has had many exciting experiences doing volunteer dental work in high need areas of Ghana, Africa, and China. Leanne can be reached at 112-200 Lincoln Way, Calgary, Alberta, Canada T3E 7G7.

Lenora P. Rutledge, RDH, graduated from East Tennessee State University in 1984. She is a dental hygienist in a group practice and resides in Kingsport, Tennessee with her husband, Bruce, and daughters, Morgan and Jamie. She enjoys biking, camping, and singing. Ms. Rutledge appears at local schools as the Tooth Fairy as she educates children in dental health methods.

Steven Schwartz, DDS, has maintained a successful pediatric dental practice since 1976. He is a Diplomate of the American Board of Pediatric Dentistry and a member of the National Speakers Association. He lectures extensively on pediatric dentistry and practice management topics. As president of WOW Enterprises, LLC, Dr. Schwartz can be reached by phone at 800-618-8819 or by email at wowsmnrs@aol.com.

Gary D. Sellers, DDS, graduated from the University of Missouri in Kansas City Dental School in 1980. He enjoys running, reading, skiing, and spending time with his three children. Dr. Sellers operates a general dentistry practice in Boulder, Colorado.

Rosalyn Shraiar, RDH, has been a dental hygienist since 1964. She says that her job as a "tooth picker" has evolved over the years into a position of "prevention care provider." You may contact Ms. Shraiar at 52 Goldcliff Road, Malden, Massachusetts 02148-1623 or by phone at 781-321-4079

Brad Shwidock, DMD, practices general dentistry in Stamford, Connecticut. He is a Fellow of the Academy of General Dentistry and Member of the American Academy of Cosmetic Dentistry. Dr. Shwidock also performs forensic dental work on a state and regional basis.

Katharine A. Simmons, RDH, has been a dental hygienist for 20 years. Since 1984, she has lived in Southern Oregon's beautiful Rogue Valley. She is married and has two teenage sons. The greatest joy and privilege of her career has been in meeting and getting to know large numbers of interesting patients through the years. Ms. Simmons may be reached at 41 Hawthorne Street, Medford, Oregon 97504 or by phone at 541-773-1042.

Susan Skipper, RDH, lives and works in the Atlanta area and has been a practicing hygienist for 16 years. She enjoys traveling and has the goal of visiting a new U.S. city every year.

Jane A. Soli died unexpectedly of a massive stroke at the age of 76 after submitting her story. The daughter of a country dentist, she was also a mother, grandmother, and great grandmother. Writing became second nature to her when she realized that no one listened when she talked—least of all her own children. Anticipating the day when they would try to recall family stories, Jane started writing them down. One of her five children is a dental hygienist. **Diane Stefanowicz, RDH,** is a graduate of Eastern Washington University and currently practices in Seattle. "Rainbow Child," her first story, was written as a tribute to her friend Melissa Porter who lost her mother, Louise Petitt, to breast cancer. Monies received for the publication of her story will be donated to the Susan G. Komen Breast Cancer Foundation. Diane may be contacted by mail at 5702 N. Hunter, Tacoma, Washington 98406, by phone at 253-759-2690, or by email at dmstefano@aol.com.

Teri Steinberg, DDS, practices dentistry with her husband, Dr. Steve. They have four wonderful children who all enjoy reading stories from the *Chicken Soup* series. Dr. Teri and Dr. Steve, co-presidents of Paradocs Speakers, often use *Chicken Soup* stories to make a point when speaking to businesses about values, purpose, and sacred service. The Dr's. Steinberg may be contacted at their Skokie, Illinois offices by fax at 847-674-0202 or by email at Paradocs22@aol.com.

Sandy Westenberger, RDH, has been a Registered Dental Hygienist for 19 years and a freelance writer "since birth." As a member of the American Dental Hygienists' Association and president-elect of the Wisconsin Dental Hygienists' Association, she has formed friendships with colleagues across the nation. These special friends inspired her to write "Prayer of the Dental Hygienist." To order a copy suitable for framing, you may call 888-RDH-WDHA.

Jay L. Wolff, DDS, is a graduate of Georgetown University and the Georgetown University Dental School. He and his wife of more than 44 years have two daughters and three grandchildren. Following his graduation from Georgetown, he served for two years in the U.S. Air Force Dental Corps and conducted a private dental practice in Oxon Hill, Maryland, for the next 27 years. In 1970, he was elected to the Pierre Fauchard Society and in 1971, he was elected a Fellow of the British Royal Society. Retired in 1987, Dr. Wolff and his wife now live in Naples, Florida.

Lawrence Yanover, DDS, PhD, received his DDS in 1977 from the University of Toronto followed by certification in pediatric dentistry in 1982 and a PhD in 1984. After teaching full time on the University of Western Ontario Faculty of Dentistry from 1984 to 1986, he established a private practice in St. Catharines, Ontario, Canada. Although most of his time is committed to his practice and family, Dr. Yanover also lectures on pediatric dentistry and is a published journalist and photographer. He may be reached by phone at 905-646-5937.

A New Season of

Chicken Soup for the Soul

Chicken Soup for
the Golden Soul
Code #7257
$12.95

Chicken Soup for the
Unsinkable Soul
Code #6986 • $12.95

Chicken Soup for the
College Soul
Code #7028 • $12.95

Chicken Soup for the
Cat and Dog Lover's Soul
Code #7109 • $12.95

Each one of these new heartwarming titles will bring inspiration
both to you and the loved ones in your life.

More from the *Chicken Soup for the Soul®* Series